Perfick!

A Celebration of the Television Series

The Darling Buds of May

LONDON · NEW YORK · SYDNEY · TORONTO

This edition published 1991 by BCA by arrangement with Bloomsbury Publishing Ltd.

CN 4932

Original television production by Yorkshire Television Limited in association with Excelsior Group Productions.

A CIP record for this book is available from the British Library

Edited and designed by Toucan Books
Printed and bound in the UK by Butler and Tanner Limited, Frome and London

Contents

Acknowledgements

The Publishers would like to thank the following for their help in creating this book:

Susan Hill, for her excellent editorial work and rewriting skills; Toucan for editorial and design; Richard Bates and Philip Burley of Excelsior Group Productions Ltd for their support; YTV, especially Filip Cieslik, and Brian Jeeves and his staff of the YTV Stills Department; and Gerald Pollinger of Laurence Pollinger Limited.

Foreword

One day, in 1956, my father handed me the type-script of his latest short story. It was something of a departure, he told me. Something quite different, something ... funny.

I read the story and agreed with him that it was certainly both different and ... funny. Those modest but telling six thousand words were to later form the first chapter of a new novel titled *The Darling Buds of May*. A novel that in turn spawned four further novels featuring the indomitable Larkins, a feature film, a radio series, a stageplay and now, most successfully of all, a television series.

What H.E. created then has stood the test of appreciation by viewers and readers all over the world and I hope that this book will serve as a happy reminder for our television audience of a series that gave us as much pleasure to make as it clearly did millions of people to watch.

Richard Bates
Executive Producer

The World of H.E. Bates

The young H.E. Bates with his mother and younger sister.

'One early summer evening Madge and I were driving through a Kentish village twenty-five miles east of us, in apple orchard country... I noticed a ramshackle lorry that had been recently painted a violent electric blue. Two or three minutes later there came out of the shop, in high spirits, a remarkable family: father a perky, sprightly character with dark side-burns, Ma a youngish handsome woman of enormous girth, wearing a bright salmon jumper and shaking with laughter like a jelly, and six children, the eldest of them a beautiful dark-haired girl of twenty or so. All were sucking at colossal multi-coloured ice creams and at the same time crunching potato crisps. As they piled into the lorry there was an air of uninhibited abandon about it all. Wild laughter rang through the village street and the whole scene might have come out of Merrie England.'

H.E. Bates's grandfather Lucas. He was a passionate countryman and an important figure in Bates's life.

Herbert Ernest Bates wrote this in the third, and last, volume of his autobiography, published in 1972. He explained that the bright image of this family group remained with him. He knew he had to write about them but it was a while before he knew how. Then, on another drive through the Kentish countryside he passed a run-down farm with its yard bestrewn with broken-down machinery, undisciplined livestock, chaotically stacked crates and a general air of cheerful neglect. He knew that the family and the farm belonged together and the idea of *The Darling Buds of May* crystallised. The book was published in 1958 and immediately became just as much a classic of English rural life, idealised, of course, as *Diary of a Nobody* is of suburban life in the 1880s. The chronicles of the Larkin tribe and the

Hop-stringing in the hop fields of Kent.

Herbert Ernest Bates

Pooter family have much in common - their gentle humour, astute social observation, the feelings of affection generated in the writing, the good-natured demolition of the stuffy and, above all, the celebration of family life.

H.E. Bates might have been surprised to see how, over thirty years later, his stories have been embraced by a whole new generation. Never out of print and appealing to a steady readership since publication, the Larkin stories could not be said to have been neglected, but the astonishing success of the Yorkshire Television series says much about Bates's sure touch when writing about human nature and enduring values. In the 1990s Pop Larkin's world seems as innocent and as far away as Camelot, and as seductive. It is a world the reader and the viewer want to believe in, would like to return to and of which, at the very least, they can have a glimpse.

H.E. Bates was born in 1905. His boyhood in Northamptonshire instilled in him a deep and abiding love of the English countryside. The family was

H.E. Bates with his family at their house in Little Chart, Kent

not well off so his pleasures were simple - walking, learning about wild flowers, bird-watching, coming to understand cloud formations, the habits of animals. Affected as an adolescent by the First World War, he began to write poetry and spent more and more time in both the public library and his schools'. Despite excelling at school and his father's willingness to make all the necessary sacrifices, Bates decided not to go to university. Neither, years later, did either of his sons. He writes that, perhaps, they were not an academically-minded family.

He left school at sixteen and worked on the local paper. By the time he was twenty his first novel, *The Two Sisters* was published and further novels appeared in 1932, 1934, 1939 and 1952, when *Love for Lydia* introduced him to a wider public. Already *Fair Stood the Wind for France* had established him as one of the finest novelists of World War Two and his short stories, based on his RAF experiences and written as Flying Officer X, had been hugely successful.

He married in 1930 and he and Madge settled in Little Chart, a village twenty miles from Canterbury. Bates's love of Kent grew steadily and from then on, apart from wartime interruptions and travels to North America and Tahiti, he was wedded to the gentle, fruitful countryside of the Garden of England. His children grew up to love it too.

It was, partially, his deep familiarity with the Kentish countryside that steeped the Larkin chronicles with such authenticity. The Larkins could, Bates wrote, if necessary be read on two planes, 'for the sheer joy of their enviable way of life, but also as a reflection on the revolution that had overtaken post-war England ... In the early thirties not a single farm worker in my village had a car, many not even a bicycle; today many have two cars, many a cottage inhabited by a family displays four, five, even six cars; few village shops sold anything but mousetrap cheese, fat bacon, candles, paraffin, tart oranges and boiled sweets; today every one has its deep-freeze

Apple-picking in Kent

The Granary, H.E. Bates's home in Little Chart, Kent.

dispensing scampi, smoked salmon, spaghetti bolognese and exotics of every kind.' Bates was writing in 1972.

The Officer Training Course and, later, active service in the RAF might have provided H.E. Bates with some early role models for Pop Larkin. He wrote of a fellow trainee who had come up through the ranks and consequently knew every dodge, every way of bending rules and every way of avoiding unnecessary unpleasantness. He described how this fellow got out of parades and square-bashing.

'It's two o'clock. Hadn't you better get ready for parade?'

'Not coming.'

'Not coming?'

'No.'

'Good God, why ever not?'

'Going out.'

'Going out? Where on earth to?'

'Dental.'

The man explained you could always get out of irksome duties if you claimed to need dental or medical attention. They couldn't touch you for it because, he reasoned, how could it be proved that there was nothing wrong after all unless you went to see the medics.

Years later Bates was friendly with a precociously young colonel who was expert in bending the rules of H.M. Customs and Excise, particularly where tobacco was concerned.

'It's a cinch, old boy. Leave it all to me. I've got the whole ruddy thing taped....Piece o' cake. Nothing to it. Leave it to me. Had all the gen in a letter from a type who flew home a couple of weeks ago. Loaded with jewels, rugs, silks, tobacco and all the riches of Samarkand and all that and just sailed through like an innocent. Never touched him for a farthing. It's all a question, old boy, of knowing the ropes.'

There seems to be a little bit of Pop in both these characters, affectionately recalled, or perhaps it is the other way round.

Returning from Burma at the end of the war, Bates wrote: 'I gazed out on England, my beloved England. Never, I kept telling myself, had it looked so beautiful. Green meadows, woods rich with golden sallow and white with the loveliest of trees, the cherry, gardens alight with daffodils and tulips and

The Bates family on holiday in Brittany. It was this holiday that inspired H.E. to write A Breath of French Air.

even, so early in the year, lilacs in pink and white blossom. This was my own, I kept telling myself, my native land, and unashamedly I let my eyes fill with tears, so that the countryside slipping by the train windows in the golden glory of evening light became a trembling evanescence of green and gold and blue It was late when I arrived home on a night as balmy as in a perfect July. The air was sweet breath on my face, the garden full of scent. I gazed for a few moments on a luxuriant bed of polyanthus that seemed like the very epitome of all that was loveliest in an English spring, then gathered my suitcase, my bed roll and my bananas...

The kitchen door was unlocked. I dumped my stuff by the stove, then tiptoed upstairs and folded a wakeful Madge in my arms.'

The war years were over, then, but they informed much of his later work and found a sublime expression in Pop Larkin, with his rackets and fiddles, army surplus deals and plots, all in the quiet beauty of the Kentish countryside that Bates had missed so much.

Richard Bates, elder son of H.E. Bates and executive producer of *The Darling Buds of May*, explained that his father actually hated Northamptonshire, although he spent a good deal of time writing about it. Bates embraced the landscape and customs of Kent with all the vigour of the converted after he and Madge found their house in Little Chart, having tramped the lanes of Kent with their rucksacks before their marriage. It had originally been a granary but the Bates's first converted it for family life and, over the years, built on to it. It remained the family home until after H.E.'s death, whereupon Madge moved into the adjacent converted cowshed.

The Bates children, Ann, Judith, Richard and Jonathan, all went to the village school and remember how wartime bombing raids disrupted lessons sometimes. Later, when *The Darling Buds of May* was enjoying its first success, pilgrims would track down the family house - rather as Peter Mayle's readers have traced his home in Provence - and expect to find Pop Larkin in the yard. Richard Bates remembers how sometimes his father would be mistaken for the gardener and the 'pilgrims' would be disappointed to find a comfortable order rather than the tangled chaos of Pop's yard.

In the late 1950s there was a stage production of *Darling Buds* starring Peter Jones and then Bernard Miles played Pop in a successful radio adaptation. When film rights were sold to MGM the stories were effectively frozen: the Hollywood version of the Larkins, filmed as *The Mating Game*, was moderately successful but MGM's ownership of the material prevented any British version being filmed or televised. Richard Bates eventually bought back the dramatisation rights and the programmes went into production soon afterwards.

He says that, unlike most of his father's fiction, the secondary characters of *Darling Buds* were often based on local Kentish people. 'I certainly knew the Brigadier', he said. More often H.E. Bates's people were not so closely modelled on real people.

'We set out to make a good quality piece of entertainment and to be faithful to the stories. We did not imagine it would be so big', Richard Bates continued. 'The timing of it helped, coming so soon after the end of the war in the Gulf, Fleet Street helped as they paid it such attention, and having David Jason playing Pop capped our success.'

But, said Richard Bates, the real key was the way the Larkin family live at the end of the rainbow. 'Making money isn't very important to Pop. He spends his money on the good things in life for his family. There's a simplicity to his life - his greatest pleasure is to have his family around him. His generosity of spirit is attractive.'

H.E. Bates wrote twenty-three novels and published several collections of short stories, a play and a number of essays and critiques. He was known as a 'writer's writer' for his sure touch with language and plotting. It is little short of miraculous how every superficially unrelated strand in each of the Pop Larkin stories binds together in the end to form a perfect, tight knot. To discover his world through the television series, or to return anew to his books, has proved to be a quiet and unexpected pleasure for millions.

The master of the Rolls. Pop and the family, and Charley still besuited, pose proudly.

EPISODE 1

The Darling Buds of May

PART ONE

Pop Larkin and the family were driving home in the second-hand gentian-blue truck. It wound through the lanes, dappled with sunlight, past orchards of apple trees.

Ma was squeezed next to Pop in the cab and the children were out in the back, singing noisily. Mariette, Montgomery, Primrose, the twins Zinnia and Petunia and little Victoria were in high spirits.

It was blazingly hot and Pop stopped for ice creams, managing to hold seven cornets and several bags of crisps at once. Back in the cab next to Ma, who was struggling to prevent a raspberry Super-Bumper from dripping onto her enormous bosom, Pop called out to his children. 'Everybody okay out there?'

'Yes Pop,' they chorused back in turn, all except his beloved eldest daughter, Mariette.

'Mariette, you okay?'

'Yes, Pop. I'm okay,' she replied after a moment.

Pop turned to Ma. 'What's up with Mariette?'

'I expect she's thinking.'

'Thinking? What's she got to think about?'

Driving the old gentian-blue truck through the lanes.

Ma was very proud of her new freezer.

'She's going to have a baby.'

'Oh,' said Pop. 'Well that don't matter. Perfick. Jolly good.' He paused briefly and called out of the window to enquire if anyone wanted crisps, deftly flicking packets through the open window when the cheer rose from the back.

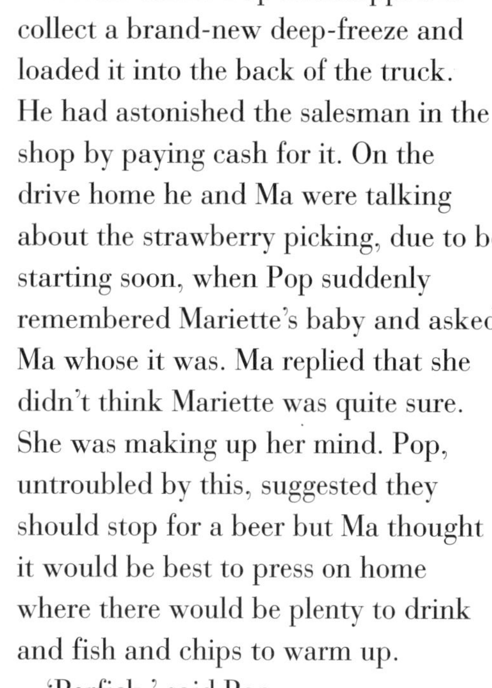

A little earlier Pop had stopped to collect a brand-new deep-freeze and loaded it into the back of the truck. He had astonished the salesman in the shop by paying cash for it. On the drive home he and Ma were talking about the strawberry picking, due to be starting soon, when Pop suddenly remembered Mariette's baby and asked Ma whose it was. Ma replied that she didn't think Mariette was quite sure. She was making up her mind. Pop, untroubled by this, suggested they should stop for a beer but Ma thought it would be best to press on home where there would be plenty to drink and fish and chips to warm up.

'Perfick,' said Pop.

The Larkin Family

Sydney Charles Larkin had met Florence Parker when she was cook and barmaid at the Three Cocks, a village a few miles away. She served him shepherd's pie and stole his heart. That was eighteen years ago when she had been a dewy seventeen-year-old and Pop a Jack the Lad with a second-hand truck and some good connections in the army surplus business. They moved in together almost immediately.

Ma seemed to get more enormous with every pregnancy and currently stood at eighteen stone. Pop, however, was as wiry as the day they'd met. He loved every surplus ounce of her and for this reason hoped that if anything she'd get fatter. The children were all named carefully and reverently, Zinnia, Petunia and Primrose after flowers, Victoria after the plum, Montgomery after the great general, Mariette after Marie Antoinette and little Oscar after a writer Ma had read about. Their home was warm, comfortable, sprawling and untidy. Pop was wild about new electrical devices, so they had the lot - a deep-freeze, four televisions, pop-up toasters and an electric kettle. Ma liked lots of bright colour around, so the decor was largely salmon pink, jade green, turquoise, lilac and orange.

After Pop and the children, cooking was Ma's passion, but despite the gargantuan meals she produced several times a day she was able, almost by magic, to keep an immaculate and spotless kitchen. On the surface of things the Larkin family was a logistical, financial and practical impossibility. In practice it was as united and warmly affectionate as any family could hope to be. Few rules, little regard for convention, eccentric hours, and an open house seemed to have provided a recipe for a rare harmony and few tears before bedtime - champagne, more likely.

Mr Cedric Charlton had a long way to go when he first met Pop Larkin and his family. But he never left Home Farm.

Meanwhile, and not far away, Mr Cedric Charlton from the Inland Revenue was also nearing journey's end. He'd travelled from town by steam train and then bus and was walking up the lane towards Home Farm. He perspired uncomfortably in his suit and wished he'd not brought his overcoat with him. But Mr Charlton was a prudent young man and liked to take no chances.

At the top of the track he'd noticed a small table where a few pots of honey and jars of wild flowers were arranged, with a card showing their prices. There was a saucer with a few coins in it and Mr Charlton, baffled, was musing on this as he walked into the yard of Home Farm.

In front of the large and badly dilapidated farmhouse was a chaotic tangle of rusty iron, old oil drums, collapsing outbuildings and pigsties. Three tethered goats were munching rubbish while chickens and ducks scratched around in the dust. He straightened his tie, picked his way across the yard and rapped firmly on the front door. No reply. Mr Charlton decided to look around the yard.

He was peering into the horsebox when the old blue truck came roaring up the track and braked, sending chickens squawking and dust flying everywhere. He watched as a small, wiry man and an enormous woman climbed from the cab; numerous children were lifted from the back by the man. Pop turned and saw him. 'Hello. Good afternoon. Looking for me?'

'Mr Sydney Charles Larkin?'

'That's me,' said Pop. 'Larkin by name, Larkin by nature.'

When Mr Charlton explained that he was a tax inspector, Pop looked blank. Mr Charlton reminded him that he had made no return of income for the past year. In fact there was no record of him having ever submitted a tax return. Pop denied any knowledge of the buff-coloured forms that Mr Charlton insisted he had been sent in the past and Ma, who dealt with the family paperwork, agreed. There must be some mistake. Mr Charlton sighed wearily and handed Pop another form but Pop recoiled from it.

'I've got no time for forms. I got pigs to feed, horses to groom, cows to milk. Tractor needs fixing, boat needs repainting. Kids to feed. And nobody ain't had no dinner.'

Mr Charlton was attempting to explain to Pop that under Section 39 of the Finance Act everyone was required to ... when Mariette crossed the yard. He caught his breath. Pop followed his gaze.

'Mariette. My eldest daughter. Mad about riding. Do you like horses, Mr ... Mr ... I never caught your name.'

'Charlton.'

Pop called Mariette over and Mr Charlton gasped as she approached.

Charley didn't stand a chance from the moment he saw Mariette.

He dropped his own buff form, dazzled by Mariette's suntanned one. 'Didn't I see you riding at Barfield. Third race. You came second.'

Pop beamed. 'This nice young man's mad about horses too Mariette. Mr Charlton, he is.'

When Mariette smiled Mr Charlton thought his glasses would steam up. He was grasping for something to say when Ma called from the kitchen that dinner was ready. Pop shrugged and began to excuse himself when he thought better of it and suggested to Mr Charlton that he should stay for dinner. That was out of the question until Mariette, too, urged him to stay.

Inside the house he felt most uncomfortable. The younger children were seated in front of great piles of fish and chips, which Mr Charlton declined. Ma was pouring tea, and lacing hers and Pop's with Johnny Walker - not his taste at all. A large television in the next room was blasting out some programme about pygmies and sending an odd grey light into the large, shadowy kitchen. The children were squealing, geese were rustling silkily under the table, Mariette was sitting opposite him and he struggled to think clearly. With an effort he tried to make Pop confront the form as Ma bustled around dishing out great bowls of ice cream. Mariette cut thick slices of fresh pineapple and Montgomery placed a jug of thick, yellow cream on the table. Mr Charlton could, he explained to Pop above the din, help him to fill it in. But after establishing that Pop was a farmer, not a dealer, that he had six children and four television sets, he got no further. Pop seemed to have no idea of his income and claimed, when pressed, to clear perhaps five pounds a week.

Ma kept interrupting with offers of food and eventually Mr Charlton admitted that he would like some boiled eggs. He watched, in a rather tormented way, as Mariette sliced the brown bread thinly for him. The children were on seconds of pineapple and ice cream, and Pop was expounding on his theory that nice safe jobs, like Mr Charlton's in the Civil Service, were all very well but it was more important to be happy, that there was no price to be put on the smell of a newly mown meadow or the song of a nightingale.

Ma was listening quietly as Pop explained that in their wood, in the mating season, the nightingales sang night and day. Mr Charlton was most surprised to learn this so Ma suggested that when he'd finished his eggs he should let Mariette take him into the woods to hear them. The very idea was intoxicating. While Mariette was changing upstairs - she'd said it was too hot for jodhpurs now - the twins announced they were going up to man their stall at the top of the track. Pop remarked proudly how everybody in his house worked, nodding towards the

Zinnia and Petunia taking care of the business.

twins with their jamjars and flowers, Montgomery milking the goats outside where Primrose and Victoria, meanwhile, were scattering corn for the birds. 'Everyone's got to work so's we can scratch a living, see? Drop o' Guinness, Mr Charlton?' Pop was reaching for the tomato ketchup to perk up his iced bun and was astonished when Mr Charlton declined more to eat or drink.

Mr Charlton was dizzy. Mariette had reappeared in a lime-green silk dress with a tight black belt and a flouncy skirt. She asked if he was ready and he followed her dumbly outside. Watching them Ma noted contentedly that he seemed to be a bit smitten and Pop, taking her in his arms, said that Mariette's luscious beauty was not to be wondered at - she was the image of Ma at that age.

As Mariette and Mr Charlton walked towards the bluebell wood, shady with great oaks, May trees and beeches, she explained that this was Pop's paradise, a cathedral of beauty. They listened to the birdsong - blackbird, wren and finally the matchless nightingale. Mariette teased him that he hadn't really believed they would hear one and teased him further that he was surprised that the girl he'd seen riding at Barfield should live at Home Farm. Mr Charlton could think of nothing but the heaven of walking on through these woods with this sublime creature and it wasn't until early evening that he and

Pop Larkin

There was a difference, somehow, between being dishonest and breaking the law ... Sydney Charles Larkin knew that well. He wouldn't dream of the former but happily and consistently did the latter. 'Whose laws?' he would have argued. 'They didn't check with me before they made them.' He didn't see any harm in a little creative dealing here and there if no one was damaged and he did himself a bit of good. He had a large family and an enormous wife to support, after all.

For Pop, life was to be enjoyed, even the working aspects of it. Food was to be enjoyed, so why scrimp? Drink was to be enjoyed, so why not have another? Ma was to be enjoyed, so let's have an early night. The countryside was Pop's church. To him the woodlands and meadows were almost holy. His pleasure in the sight and scent of the flowers, the sound of birdsong, the silky feel of a horse's flank were almost sensuous. Surrounded as he was by the things he loved, both in his home and in the rich land around it, it was no surprise that he was a happy man. He was also a loyal friend and the fondest of fathers, someone who rarely made an enemy. People, who often misjudged him on first acquaintenceship, were quickly won over by his wit, shrewd intelligence and charm.

His energy, philosophical good humour, audacity and a generous measure of good luck had brought Pop Larkin the life he loved. He got back, in short, roughly what he put into it. A perfick deal.

Mariette returned to the farmhouse, carrying bunches of bluebells and pink campion.

Ma had cleared up in the kitchen and Pop had killed three geese for Sunday lunch. Without actually saying very much they had both thought about Mariette and Mr Charlton. Pop had murmered 'Perfick' several times. It was time for tea when they returned, which confused Mr Charlton who had thought he had barely finished lunch. No, Ma corrected him, that was dinner, and she would brook no argument about him staying. Feebly Mr Charlton took the opportunity of again asking Pop about his tax return but Pop had just seen some goldfinches, so that was that.

With the television still thundering in the next room the family was seated again. Ma brought in a huge dish of plump kippers and was talking to Pop about the forthcoming strawberry picking; he remarked that the new deep-freeze would come in handy for the fruit. When Mr Charlton began enquiring about capital expenditure on new deep-freezes Pop claimed he'd taken it as a debt and poured a healthy slug of whisky into his tea.

'Look here, Mr Charlton, what's your other name? Don't like all this "mistering".'

'Cedric.'

Ma shook like a jelly at this, almost choking with laughter, and Pop, disguising his own embarrassment, asked Mr Charlton if he'd like to play a few hands of crib. He airily dismissed the other's protestations that he had to get home by informing him that the last bus was long gone and he might as well stay the night, topping up Mr Charlton's tea with whisky and exclaiming, when pressed, that there was plenty of time to talk about the tax form later.

That evening Charley, as Pop decided his new friend should be called, was introduced to the mysteries of cribbage under the guidance of Pop, Ma and Mariette. Pop had been mixing some of his most lethal cocktails over the course of the evening and Charley was feeling distinctly odd. At some stage it had been agreed that he would sleep in the billiard room and borrow a pair of Mariette's pyjamas. 'Perfick,' Pop said, 'perfick.' He reckoned it was time for another cocktail, perhaps a new one, the Rolls Royce, Pop thought. It was half vermouth, quarter whisky, quarter gin with a dash of orange bitters. Pop mixed it in double quantities, to save time, as he always said. Charley squinted. From here the cocktail cabinet looked exactly like a Spanish galleon. Quite right, Pop informed him. Exclusive design.

'My God, this is a perfick pick-me-up,' said Pop eyeing his drink.

'A few more of these and you won't see me for dust,' beamed Ma.

'A few more? A few more?' said Charley weakly. The other three all began laughing at something Pop said and when Pop slapped him on the back he joined in, not even knowing what the joke was. He'd never felt like this, so enveloped in goodwill and unrestrained pleasure. The drink was the elixir of life, Mariette's perfume was divine, these people were god-like in their kindness. He swung his arms, attempting an expansive gesture, fell over backwards and landed on the floor.

'You're a rattling good feller. Feel you're one of the family. Feel we've known you for years. That right, Ma?'

That night Mariette put Charley to bed in the billiard room. He went to sleep in a happy delirium but with no subsequent memory of how he had got into Mariette's pyjamas.

By the time he emerged in the morning the Larkin family had been up for hours, Pop in the yard contemplating another perfick day, the children busy with their chores, Mariette riding in the buttercup fields and Ma fixing enormous breakfasts of eggs, bacon, sausage, mushrooms and fried bread. Charley felt very unwell, barely able to contemplate a cup of tea and the sight of Pop attacking his second breakfast of the day didn't help. Even the sight of Mariette didn't cheer him. 'I really do think I'd better go home.'

Pop put an arm round his shoulder. 'All you need Charley boy, is a Larkin special. Just the thing.' He busied himself with raw eggs and various spirits and Worcester sauce. Charley was looking for his buff form, unaware that Ma had already disposed of it with the rest of the rubbish, as Pop set the concoction in front of him. With great reluctance he drank the killer cure, but only minutes later, walking with Mariette, who had dragged him outside, he knew that Pop was right. His head felt better already.

'I think I'll ask Charley to stay for lunch,' said Ma.

'Perfick,' said Pop.

Mariette had taken Charley down to the lake and they took the boat out. He told her about his parents dying in a bombing raid when he was six and about his aunt who brought him up. By the time they got back to the house Pop had returned from a very special errand - at the wheel of a yellow, pre-war Rolls-Royce with monogrammed doors.

'Royal?' asked Ma.

'Duke I think. Feller I got it off don't know. Some toff.' Pop patiently explained to Charley that he got it through a deal, and only partly in cash. He never had, he said, enough cash in hand long enough to need to pay any tax. Stands to reason. Having sorted that out he called everyone over to the Rolls to climb in. They were going for a ride down to the village where, had he but known it, he was the subject of a heated debate in the village hall.

A disaster had befallen the

Pop Larkin took the Rolls in part payment of a debt.

gymkhana committee. Mr Fortescue had withdrawn the use of his field for the forthcoming event and the committee chairman, Edith Pilchester, was struggling to maintain order. She was meeting opposition to her plan to ask Syd Larkin to lend his meadow. The man was a spiv, it was too shaming to have to ask him, the whole family was a disgrace to the village, he dealt on the black market ... the objections went on and on.

At last, when Edith had made it clear they had no other options, there was grudging assent and the Brigadier, a latecomer to the meeting, was deputed to approach Larkin. It was an astonished committee who saw Pop and the family drive regally past the hall as their meeting dispersed.

Pop tooted the horn. 'Afternoon! Perfick weather, ain't it?'

'Good God,' said Edith Pilchester.

On Sunday morning, three geese in the oven, six or seven different kinds of vegetable ready to go, the long table under the walnut tree laid by Mariette and Charley, lunch was well underway. Earlier Pop had shown Charley three hundred tins of pickled gherkins stacked in the barn and asked if he knew anyone who would like them. Charley had been unable to help, but undeterred Pop sauntered off to polish the Rolls with Montgomery. 'We've got a visitor, Pop.'

It was the Brigadier. Pop had a little bet with himself that the old boy was

Charley

Cedric Charlton's parents were killed in the Blitz when he was six. His dear Aunt Bridget brought him up in Harrow. She was as kind and loving as any aunt could be, but inevitably young Cedric grew up with a sense of insecurity. It was thus not surprising when, after university, he chose that steadiest of all professions - the Civil Service. Cedric was doing well as a trainee tax inspector under the guidance of his mentor, Mr Shell, in the Canterbury office, when the Larkins exploded into his life and changed it for ever.

Even his physical appearance changed after a while on Home Farm. The pale face grew tanned, his chest and arms became muscular and his mousy hair was bleached by the sun. He seemed to become taller, wore his glasses less often. Most of all, his bearing changed. There was a purpose in his stride and a lift to his chin - a confidence that hadn't existed before. Maybe this was simply because of Mariette and his enduring sense of disbelief and pride that she had chosen him. Maybe. And maybe it was partly to do with his total adoption by a great, warm, noisy family. He felt that he had come home at last.

A city boy, he found he loved every aspect of living in the country. The woods and flowers, the lanes and tracks, horse-riding, fruit picking, learning about livestock, getting to know the eccentrics in the neighbourhood, Ma's wonderful cooking, Pop's lethal cocktails ... he took to it all like a duck to orange. And it wasn't all one-sided. Pop came to rely on him increasingly when a bit of business here or a deal there called for some brain-work. It was a fair and equal exchange. Everyone was happy - Charley perhaps most of all, as Pop took such happiness for granted and Charley saw it as a great and unexpected gift.

after a donation to some charity. 'General, what can I do for you?' He always addressed the Brigadier as General. The old man was briefly distracted by the Rolls and resisted the temptation to ask how Pop could afford it. His resistance to Pop's offer of a snifter was more easily overcome.

Seated in the living room with a large whisky and soda he came straight to the point about Pop's meadow and the gymkhana. Pop agreed at once. The Brigadier urged him to think about it.

'Good grief, nothing to decide. The meadow's there, isn't it. All I got to do is get the grass cut. Perfick.'

Pop replenished his own glass and the Brigadier's. Ma came in from the kitchen and hearing that he was on his own that day, his sister being out, insisted that the Brigadier stay for lunch. 'Can't have you eating cold on Sunday.'

The Brigadier made a half-hearted stab at declining, but Pop's insistance and the fragrance of roasting geese coming from the kitchen were very persuasive. 'Perfick,' said Pop. 'The more the merrier.'

Ma went back to the kitchen and saw Mariette and Charley sitting under the walnut tree. That's all very well, she thought, *talking*. But when's he going to do something more, well, technical? She thought about her visitors as she stirred apple sauce. Half starved, the pair of them. Charley needs beefing up and the General, well, she was sure his sister starved him. Pop interrupted her reverie with a grab round her waist. After a minute she pushed him away with a laugh. 'I've got mouths to feed, remember.'

Pop introduced Charley and the Brigadier, explaining about the tax lark. 'Tried to rope me into that swindle. I should like, eh General? What do you say?' The Brigadier sadly said it was all academic for him as his income was so tiny. He asked Charley if he was a house guest and Charley, wonderingly, replied that yes, he supposed in a way he was.

Lunch was magnificent. The geese, asparagus, green peas, onions, different kinds of potatoes, red port, white port, wines, strawberries, Jersey cream ... the Brigadier had not eaten so well in years. Pausing once, he asked Pop if he'd told the children about the gymkhana, so Pop announced the news. The squeals of excitement matched the racket the piglets put up. Mariette ran round the table to kiss her father and tell him over and over what a lovely man he was. She kissed the Brigadier too when Pop told her that it was really his idea. Then she kissed Ma and to his unimaginable delight she kissed Charley as well. He thought he was in heaven. Pop asked the Brigadier about the other members of the committee and nodded as the names were listed. No great friends of his there. And Edith Pilchester, of course,

Mariette kissed Charley for the first time when Pop agreed to the gymkhana.

the Brigadier remembered.

'Oh Edith. I love old Edith. She's a sport,' Pop grinned.

'You be careful there,' warned Ma with mock severity.

'Perfickly harmless.'

'Splendid organiser,' said the Brigadier.

But the others, no. Mrs Peele and George Carter and Freda O'Connor ... 'Always showing off her bosom. She's a tart,' Ma pronounced. 'And that Jack Woodley is a complete bar-' continued Pop before Ma stopped him with a glare. 'Not in front of the children Pop.'

As they were eating the ice cream Ma, who had had a little talk to Mariette in the kitchen and had hatched a plan, steered the subject round to the strawberry-picking to come and suggested that Charley stay down for the rest of the week. It would do him good, she said. He could take some sick leave. Pop thought this was a splendid idea. Charley could make fifteen or twenty pounds a day and with all the money he must have paid into the health service, wasn't it time that he had a little lay-off?

Using words like 'adamant' and 'prejudice', Charley said he couldn't, he just couldn't. Ma and Pop persisted but Charley wouldn't be budged. Eventually Mariette and Ma went indoors with the dishes leaving the men outside. When Mariette emerged a little later with tea things Pop looked up proudly as she walked across the grass. 'My God, Charley, ain't she beautiful?'

'Oh yes, yes, she is.'

Over his tea, mellower than ever, Pop reflected on how perfick everything was, how every sight that met his gaze was wonderful and began thinking ahead to the gymkhana. 'It would be wonderful if the gymkhana was as perfick. Perhaps we should have fireworks ...' He saw that the Brigadier had fallen asleep over his tea and that Ma was nodding off. Looking up at the perfect sky he remarked pointedly to Charley that he didn't know how people could work in offices. Charley felt disquieting doubts, too.

Pop was drawing on a fat cigar and asked Charley to put one in the

Under the walnut tree at Home Farm. Sunday lunch for the Larkin family with the Brigadier and Charley.

Brigadier's hand. 'And then we'll go,' said Mariette.

'Go where?' asked Charley.

'To the woods. It might be our last chance.'

'Good idea.' Pop looked fondly at the two of them. 'Perfick.' He watched Mariette take Charley's arm as they walked across the grass towards the woods.

'I didn't think anything could be like this. All of it. Pop. Ma. You ...'

'Shall you come strawberry-picking tomorrow?'

'I've already explained...'

'Shall you come?' Mariette touched Charley's hand lightly.

'Yes.' He couldn't resist any longer. 'Yes! Yes! Yes!'

Working in the strawberry fields was Charley's first taste of physical labour. He takes a little rest with Mariette.

EPISODE 2

The Darling Buds of May

PART TWO

It was another perfect May morning in the Garden of England. Pop had eaten his first breakfast and lovingly inspected his domain, as usual. The children had gone about their chores - milking and feeding of livestock and birds - and Mr Charlton thought his heart would break as he stared at them from his window.

He knotted his tie. Dawn had brought a change of heart. Gathering his briefcase and overcoat and glancing around the room, he walked down to the kitchen. Ma and Pa looked dismayed to see him dressed for the office. 'Going back to work, old man? You said you were coming with us. We're all going. Kids are staying off school ...' Pop was bemused. Charley tried to explain that his promise to go strawberry-picking was a folly of the moment, a dream that daylight could not sustain. He mumbled something about the tax office being his career, his life, about being sensible. Ma repeated that he could do with some sick leave, if anyone asked her. Charley bridled. No one would ever accuse him of abusing the benefits of the welfare state. Ma was just telling him that he had some nasty-looking white spots on his cheekbones when the lovely Mariette walked straight in, flushed from her ride.

She glanced at him. 'You'll be much too hot dressed like that.' When she heard of Charley's decision to return to town she became angry. He had

The diminutive Aunt Fran went strawberrying with the family.

promised, she reminded him. He was disappointing the whole family, behaving as if they didn't count.

Ma and Pop were a little embarrassed and Ma broke a strained silence by asking Charley what he wanted for breakfast. But Charley had leapt up to follow Mariette outside. There it took only one long look of hurt and longing from her great dark eyes to finish his resolve forever.

They'd all piled into the gentian-blue truck, picked up tiny Aunt Fran and sung pop songs all the way to the strawberry farm. Brown and shiny as a nut, Aunt Fran had a voice that could break glass and a cackle like a hyena, and she made quite a bit of fun of Charley. When they arrived Pop muttered something about going off to Portsmouth to do some business and Charley remembered to remind Pop to deliver his letter pleading illness to his office on the way.

The sight of the fields and the hard physical labour ahead made Charley lose his nerve. He was greatly relieved when, shortly afterwards, the man in the tent where the pickings were weighed and paid for suggested that Charley take over the admin work. A couple of boxes filled at Mariette's side had shown that he didn't yet have the back and brawn for this work and he couldn't strip off his shirt, as Mariette had suggested, for fear of catcalls from the women in the field.

Yes, he felt much more comfortable in the cool of the tent. He was good with figures, after all. But he wasn't terribly good with women, not yet. A tall girl called Pauline, skin-tight in black, came in with her first load and gave Charley a look which made his neck sweat. Then came two older women, both leathery from heat and wind and flinty-eyed from years of honest cheating, who successfully made him pay them for many more pounds of berries than they had picked. Later they did it again and finally asked him to lend them money. His head was spinning. Ma and the younger children came in with their pickings and left him an iced lolly which he was too flustered to unwrap.

Charley didn't really like the effort of strawberry-picking.

Mariette

Mariette was the Larkins' eldest child. Every time he looked at her, Pop was reminded of how Ma had looked when she, too, was seventeen ... tall, olive-skinned, flashing dark eyes, lustrous black hair and a figure that made male drivers crash into hedges when they encountered her in the lanes on her black mare.

Mariette was crazy about horses, always had been. She raced at point-to-points, hunted to hounds and rode every morning across the buttercup fields. She was quite keen on boys, too, and until she met Charley was toying with the affections of at least three young men in the area. Pop hadn't been unduly worried. He thought it was all perfickly natural.

Like all the Larkins she had a very healthy appetite but colossal amounts of food made no difference to her slenderly voluptuous figure. Charley sometimes looked at her and then at Ma and wondered when the day of reckoning would come. He was sure he wouldn't mind when it did, any more than Pop had.

Ma was very particular about names for all her children and, having an interest in tragic historical queens, was all set to call her first-born Marie Antoinette. Pop had baulked at this, saying it was far too long, and Mariette had been the happy compromise. Like her father, she was passionately in tune with nature and knew every flower, every individual birdsong, every animal track in the wood and every constellation in the sky. She made Pop the proudest father in Kent and Charley the happiest husband.

Strawberry-picking was a nice little earner for some.

Just before it began to melt Pauline returned with more fruit.

After finding out that yes, his real name was Cedric but that he was called Charley and that he was sort of on holiday and staying with the Larkins and bruising her wide mouth with several large crushed strawberries, she moved in on the iced lolly. Charley was happy to let her have it and she languidly licked it, lolling on the edge of his work-table.

Charley had just begun to grasp what her intentions might be when Mariette walked in. The two girls exchanged hostile glances and Pauline stalked off.

'Tart,' Mariette hissed at her departing back.

'Steady. She'll hear you.'

'She's meant to!'

Charley tried in vain to explain that this was a big fuss to make over an iced lolly but Mariette simply looked at him pityingly and returned to the fields. Charley didn't have time to ponder on this as Poll and Lil, the jovial con women, were back with yet more berries for weighing.

Good as his word, Pop had stopped off to deliver Charley's letter at the Inland Revenue office in the town where Charley worked. No trouble, really. It was on the way to Portsmouth. He did, however, have a nasty moment. A Mr Shell, Charley's boss, took the letter and started asking Pop, first if he knew Mr Charlton (No, said Pop - feller gave him the note in the pub), and secondly if he happened to know if said Mr Charlton was with one Syd Larkin. Pop, who had taken the precaution of calling himself Ernie Partridge, denied all knowledge of anyone called Larkin. Mr Shell, who had not worked in a tax office all his life without developing something of a nose for these things, was no more convinced by this than he was by Mr Charlton's claim to be smitten by lumbago. This Partridge fellow was distinctly shifty.

Pop had a nasty moment with Charley's old boss, Mr Shell.

Shell launched into a long speech about social parasites and moral reprobates, using lots of long words that Pop didn't understand. Shell was by now addressing his speech to an imaginary audience outside the office window. Pop took his chance and ran.

Back in the strawberry fields Charley was getting the hang of things. In a brief pause from weighing and registering loads he dunked his head in a bucket of cold water thoughtfully brought by Primrose and Montgomery. Looking outside he thought he needed another. In the strong late-afternoon heat almost all the women had stripped off their blouses and were at work in the fields in their brassières, bending low to expose cleavages which ranged from massive ones like Ma's, voluptuous ones like Pauline's and funny little withered ones like Aunt Fran's. He had to turn back inside.

To his horror Pauline stepped in, resplendent in a lacy black bra, cut very low. She said she'd had enough for the day, thought she might go for a swim and suggested that Charley came with her. Charley didn't know how to respond. He didn't want to seem rude. Pauline left him with a suggestive stretch and the threat of coming back later to fetch him. He had an idea that Mariette watched Pauline sashaying out of the tent.

The afternoon wore on, hotter and hotter. After yet another visit from Poll and Lil, Charley's concentration was shattered by the sounds of shrieks and shouting. He followed Poll and Lil outside and saw that a circle of women had formed. Within the circle two girls were fighting, fighting pretty dirty. There was blood everywhere, flailing arms, feet kicking, nails scraping. And oh God, it was Mariette and Pauline. The other women were calling and screaming encouragements. Against his will Charley looked on, fascinated, for a little while and even let Aunt Fran sit on his shoulders to get a better view. Then he shouted 'I've got to stop them. What on earth are they fighting for?' Aunt Fran gave him a scornful look.

'Gawd almighty, don't you know, Mister? Don't you know?'

On the way home, fight over and Mariette cleaned up a bit, Charley did at last have a glimmer of what it was all about. He could still barely

Mariette and Pauline vie for Charley's favours.

comprehend that Mariette had been fighting for *him.*

Back at Home Farm, waiting for the beef to finish roasting, Pop told Ma about his day's work. He'd done a deal over a minesweeper - good bit of scrap, that. In the long grasses outside Mariette and Charley embraced and Ma needed to have no worries now about Mr Charlton's technique.

The gymkhana was uppermost in Pop's mind. He watched the final mowing of the meadow with Edith Pilchester and assured her that his other field could be used as a car park. 'All we want is a fine day. If it's wet it will be absolutely ghastly,' she said.

What a worry-guts Edith was, Pop thought. 'Can't control the water, I'm afraid. But what about a drop of whisky, drop of gin. Come on Edith, you've earned it.' He led her back to Home Farm.

Edith left some time later with a

chicken from Ma. Pop offered her a lift home in the Rolls and she was easily persuaded. Pop even suggested that she sat in the back and called out 'Home, James'-type instructions through the trumpet but Edith liked the idea of sitting in front with Pop much, much more. They arrived at Bonnybanks, Edith's small, thatched and shabby cottage, with its ill-kempt garden. She asked Pop in for a drink, certain there was some of that whisky left.

The interior was dark and chilly, even after this scorching day, and the place was full of dusty clutter, unwashed dishes and the evidence of Edith's passion for weaving - scraps of fleece and half-spun bits of twine together with pots containing the vegetable dyes she mixed herself.

'So sorry it's rather ghastly in here. Don't look. I'll get us a drink.' She swept up the indeterminate remains of some previous meal and hurried into the kitchen where she searched for that bottle with its last inch of Scotch, saved since Easter. She added an inch of water and poured them each a measure. Pop was amazed, as he looked around the living room, that anyone could live like this, let alone a an educated woman like Edith.

'No television?' he asked when Edith returned.

Edith loved being driven home by Pop in the Rolls.

'Couldn't possibly afford it.' Edith went on to explain how she had employed someone to clean and a chap for the garden before the war, but that her savings were pretty much gone now and she'd had some bad luck with War Stock. Yes, she'd had better times, but you just had to get by, didn't you. Pop was forced to agree, and mindful of his empty glass said he'd best be leaving.

'Must you?' cried Edith 'You know you've been an absolute lamb about the field. Don't know how ...' Pop stopped her with a warm hug and a smacking kiss on the lips which left Edith trembling.

'How about one more?' said Pop when they drew apart.

'Please.'

He wrapped her in his arms again. 'Perfick.'

'Did you kiss her?' Ma enquired when he returned.

'Course I did.'

'Thought you would. Make her sleep all the sweeter.'

Edith need not have worried. Gymkhana day was as perfect as any other that May. After the mowing Pop, with Charley's help, had overseen the arrangement of poles and posts, fences and tea stands, toilets and the marquee. The little ones were already near sick with excitement.

Pop looked proudly over the meadow and misunderstood the glazed look in Charley's eyes. At first he assumed that the lovely, gaily ordered sight of the field was tugging at Charley's throat, but then the great nelly started up again about income tax and how the strawberry-pickers really ought to pay some.

For once he became a little exasperated. 'If the produce never got picked it would never get to Covent Garden. There'd be riots in the streets. The Government would fall. There wouldn't be nothing. No berries, no apples, no cherries, no hops, no beer. No beer!' From Charley's pained expression Pop had faint hopes that the message had seeped through.

Some days earlier Pop had hit upon the idea of holding a party - very select - after the gymkhana. 'Cocktail party. Sort of round the day off.' Ma thought this a splendid idea, though neither she nor Pop had ever been to one. She thought it would be lovely in the billiard room and they took Charley's advice about drinks and such. Pop thought about mixing some of his most imaginative cocktails; Charley suggested champagne and perhaps a couple of other, simple, drinks, canapés and vol-au-vents but Ma thought a big, sweet ham might be nicer. Charley became worried about the cost of champagne and Pop laughed like a drain. 'No problem if you've been supplying a certain local hotel with pheasants for years, is it?'

Charley wrote all the invitations in

Edith Pilchester

Poor Edith Pilchester was not a well-favoured woman. From the age of sixteen she had worn a spinsterly air and now, in her forties, she had completely stopped hoping that a nice gentleman would walk into her life. Except, that, is, where Pop Larkin was concerned. Pop had a very soft spot for Edith. A sport, he called her, and now and again he patted her backside, gave her a cuddle and - bliss - the occasional hearty smacker on the lips. That would put Edith in a dither for days.

Like the Brigadier, Edith lived in genteel poverty. Her thatched cottage looked pretty, if ill-tended, from the outside but indoors it was chilly and dark, poky and rather grubby. Edith had never really learned about housework, as she'd grown up in a household with a huge staff and had employed, up till the war, a woman who cleaned and a man for the garden. These days she eked out a frugal living from her savings and from the sales of the curiously hideous garments she made from spinning her own wool and which she coloured with homemade vegetable dyes.

Edith was a stalwart of the Parish Council and many local committees. Many people mistakenly took her for a busy-body. Pop knew differently - she was a great organiser, a staunch friend and, when she'd had a few, quite a little raver. Ma was always worried that she didn't get enough to eat and it was rare for Pop to visit her without a parcel of ham, perhaps some eggs and a big slab of fruit tart from Ma.

Whenever Pop passed her in the lanes in his Rolls he always stopped and gave her a lift home and Edith was in heaven. It reminded her of her long-lost high life, there was the great pleasure of sitting at Pop's side ... and there was always that delicious chance that Pop would scoop her in his arms for a kiss.

his fine, cultured hand. It made Pop pause for thought and say to Ma that he began to wonder if there wasn't some point in all that education malarky after all. Then, becoming a bit rheumy, he pondered what would happen if Mariette really was sweet on him and Charley wanted to take her away.

Ma smiled to herself. 'What makes you think he wants to take her anywhere? I don't think he knows she's having someone else's baby yet.'

Shortly before gymkhana day Pop drove to Bluff Court, the local Big House. Pop wasn't sure if it was Tudor, Georgian, Jacobean or what. All he knew was that it was old and big and ought to be pulled down, however historical it might be. He'd come to deliver an invitation to the party to Sir George Bluff-Gore and his lady wife. Pop's eyes gleamed with pleasure as he thought about the scrap value of the place, glancing at the overgrown grounds and noting the dreadful disrepair of the house itself. No one answered the bell and he was turning to leave when Sir George strode up the gravel behind him.

Pop explained about the gymkhana and the party and Sir George took the invitation with distaste, as if it was some tradesman's calling card. He deigned to explain that Pop was lucky to have caught him at the main house: they lived in the lodge these days as they simply couldn't afford to run the manor any more. A hundred tons of coal to heat in winter, impossible gardeners' bills, that sort of thing.

'Might be able to do you a favour, old man. Make you an offer for it.'

Sir George was affronted. No, no. He'd never sell the family pile. Out of the question. And in any case, how on earth would a fellow like Larkin be able to afford it? Pop explained that he'd pull it down and sell off the scrap piecemeal. No wish to live there but he could see some potential. No point in an empty house, after all, was there? And he'd be able to do a cash deal.

Pop noticed a pallor creep across Sir George's face, reminded him about the party and sauntered back to the Rolls.

The gymkhana was, of course, a huge success. Finest in years, the Brigadier said. All the local children and their ponies had taken part. Ma strolled around in a queenly way resplendent in bright blue silk. Mariette looked sensational in classic, tailored rig. Pop wore a very natty brown checked suit and made sure everyone had enough ice cream. Edith had been coerced into taking part in the ladies' donkey derby and had gone and won it. She was positively skittish with Pop afterwards, imploring him not to be naughty and produce fireworks later.

When a girl begs you not to, thought Pop, it usually means that she's got other ideas. He reminded Edith that he thought that now and again she liked a

The gymkhana in Pop's meadow was the best for years. Ma and the younger girls.

bit of naughtiness, like when he'd taken her home in the Rolls. Edith collected herself and made Pop swear that there wouldn't be so much as a tuppenny banger.

His thoughts were interrupted by the Brigadier.

'Don't say this lightly, Larkin. You're a gentleman.'

Pop was bemused. 'What me? That'll be the day, General.'

A little group of the local toffs had gathered nearby. Sir George was being fawned upon by Freda and Jack Woodley. He looked around uneasily for his wife, as Freda opined that it was perfectly dreadful that they had to to hold the event here, so close to that awful slum, Home Farm, and how it really had been the lastest, lastest resort. Sir George thought he saw his lady wife taking tea with that Larkin fellow. He couldn't be sure, the light was so bright.

In fact Lady Bluff-Gore was doing a spot of dealing herself. Between them she and Pop were hatching a really spiffy plot: she would convince Sir George that if they sold Bluff Court to Larkin they'd make enough money to buy a lovely villa in Spain for the winter and be able to keep the Lodge on for the glorious Kentish summers, and Pop had offered her a premium, so

After persuasion from Pop Edith entered the ladies' donkey derby, and won.

Mariette always looked magnificent on a horse.

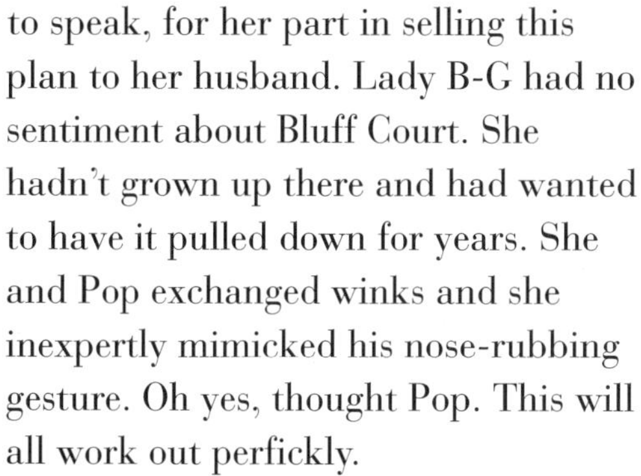

to speak, for her part in selling this plan to her husband. Lady B-G had no sentiment about Bluff Court. She hadn't grown up there and had wanted to have it pulled down for years. She and Pop exchanged winks and she inexpertly mimicked his nose-rubbing gesture. Oh yes, thought Pop. This will all work out perfickly.

Home Farm looked almost continental. Lights were strung from house to tree, from tree to shed and there were people spilling from the crush and heat of the billiard room into the garden. They drank champagne in the light breeze of this lovely starry night. Indoors there was a noisy, smokey clamour of dozens more people than Pop and Ma had invited. They were hosing down the champagne and cocktails (Pop hadn't been able to resist showing off his skills as a barman). Ma's wonderful food was passed around by the younger children, marshalled by Mariette, and there was dancing to the music that the radiogram blasted out.

Pop spotted the little Barnwell sisters, so poor and so genteel - tiny old dears too proud to ask for a ham sandwich. He brought them a whole plate and mixed them a cocktail which he christened on the spot Ma Chérie. 'Just a soda with flavouring,' he

Ma Larkin

Ma Larkin enjoyed a joke and when she laughed she shook like a jelly. Her chins wobbled, her massive bosom heaved up and down and the flesh on her arms quivered as she clapped her hands. It did Pop good just to look at her. He'd thought she was an absolute corker when they met and now she was more than twice the woman. Pop considered himself a very lucky man.

Ma was sensuous too, more so as she got older. She often suggested a little lie-down in the afternoon and some mornings she detained him in their bedroom for so long that Pop had to miss his first breakfast. Those were the mornings that Pop brought up a bottle of champagne to enhance the mood.

She might have been large, but she cared a great deal about her appearance. She chose her clothes with care for their flamboyance of cut and brightness of colour and always wore scent - Chanel No 5 or Gardenia - even if she was only spending the morning in the kitchen making jam or trussing chickens.

She had endless patience with all her children although she was very strict about their manners. She would not tolerate rudeness or disrespect. The generosity of her spirit was as massive as her bulk. If she took to someone Home Farm was an open house and she was a friend for life.

But for all this Ma Larkin was a shrewd and clever woman. She could sniff out pretentiousness, dishonesty, greed and meanness of spirit. And she did not like any of those things. It was easy, some had thought, to put one over on Ma and they had learned to their cost that she was not to be underestimated.

explained before fixing a mixture of sherry, large slugs of brandy and a dash of soda water for manners. The old girls liked it hugely and had two or three more before they set off unsteadily for their cottage in full agreement that they should ask Mr Larkin for the recipe.

Mariette was hoping to fatten the Brigadier up a little. He protested weakly, took some more ham and opined 'Damn good party. Damn fine.' Mariette thought she saw a tear glisten, but just then Charley grabbed her hand and took her outside. The Brigadier watched affectionately as they slipped into the darkness. He raised his glass to them.

Charley made a mess of it in the garden, going on about how he'd been a complete blob until he'd met Mariette and the family. How he knew he was a somebody at last.

'You are to me.'

'I've never been so happy, but to go on being happy, well, it's impossible unless ...'

'Unless?'

'I love you Mariette. Will you marry me?'

She said yes. She said yes please. They kissed and wept and kissed again.

Back in the house Pop did his duty. It wasn't actually a very painful one and when dear old Edith asked for a kiss he was happy to oblige. 'Just what the doctor ordered,' giggled Edith. 'I don't suppose there's time for one more?' Pop kissed her again. It wasn't actually so terrible and as they drew apart Edith looked up at him wildly, thanked him for the day, the gymkhana, the party, said how happy it had all made her and broke into sobs.

Pop watched the party swinging, saw Ma sashaying across the floor and was thinking how marvellous she looked when a tawny blonde figure came to rest against him. He looked up - she was quite tall - and she introduced herself as Angela Snow, apologising for gatecrashing in the same breath. Well, thought Pop, she is a stunner. What toff girls ought to look like, as slim and sleek and fair and wicked as a young racehorse. She extended a cool hand. Pop started to introduce himself but Angela Snow said there was no need. Pop was a legend and she knew all about him. She raised an elegant eyebrow towards the dance floor. 'Shall we?'

Pop was lost. From then on Angela Snow was part of his family. She might be a bit out of his class but it didn't seem to matter. They delighted in each other. And her laugh made his toes tingle. She was another good sport. Angela seemed to read his mind and asked if he liked fireworks. He dimly remembered his promise to Edith that there would be no unpleasantness of that sort, but when Angela took his hand he didn't quite seem to know

Fireworks at the party after the gymkhana.

what was what.

They gathered the fireworks and the matches and set about whizz-banging. Ma laughed her jelly shake and said she always knew he would. All over the room, in the garden, and uncomfortably near Edith Pilchester's hand-woven skirt ... a great fury of bangs and flashes which precipitated a stampede to the open air.

'I knew this would happen. It's absolutely ghastly,' said Edith.

In the garden, a little later, with further fireworks from Pop rocketing over their heads, Ma and Mariette were having a little chat. They both looked fairly perky, thought Pop, when he glimpsed them. Then Mariette raced across the grass, grabbed Charley's arm, rushed up to Pop and insisted they had a word. 'Ma says I can marry Mariette if you'll let her.' Charley could hardly speak, just gabbled.

'Let her? Of course I'll let her. Perfick.' Mariette hugged her father and asked him to announce it. It would go well with all the rockets and Catharine wheels to come, Pop thought. Perfect timing. Pop climbed onto a table and silenced everyone with a particularly nasty banger. He felt an odd mixture of pride and regret. 'Ladies, gentlemen, friends. Mr Charlton is going to wed my daughter, Mariette. Now, has everyone got their glasses filled? Give you a toast.'

'Give you a toast,' whispered Angela Snow.

Rather later Pop and Ma were preparing for bed, she in her usual flimsy, transparent kind of nightdress and he with a big cigar and a bottle of champagne on ice. Pop liked to watch Ma in those nighties of hers. Ma asked him about Angela. She thought she seemed to be a bit of a card. Pop feigned a kind of indifference that neither fooled nor worried Ma. She asked him if he fancied a late snack but Pop declined. He didn't even want any port. Ma now began to be worried. Pop seemed worried and that was most unusual.

She alluded to the gurgling noises that were coming from Charley and Mariette in the living room. 'He's certainly come on.'

Pop sighed. 'Nice about them ...

except ...'

'Except what?'

'Well, does Charlie know about the baby?'

'She's not going to have a baby now. False alarm.'

'Jolly good,' said Pop, very much brighter. 'Perfick.' His appetite was returning already.

'I am, though,' announced Ma.

Mariette and Charley ask for Pop's blessing.

Pop was given out one short of his fifty. The vicar was his batting partner.

EPISODE 3

When the Green Woods Laugh

PART ONE

Pop stood in his meadow, a shotgun in his hands and a glass of beer at his feet. He fancied wild duck on Sunday and had sent the twins to raise an alarm by Sir George's lake. With any luck some birds would fly over his land and he'd pop them. There were a couple of tense moments, but nothing doing so far. He took a long swig of his beer and gazed round his verdant domain. All was green and scented; the grass was not yet scorched and the fruit was starting to ripen. 'Perfick,' he thought, as he breathed a draught of the heady summer air.

Alerted by a quacking overhead, he set his glass down and reached for his old gun. Too late. Pop popped twice, but the birds flew safely away and into his wood. Pop couldn't really begrudge them their freedom. He finished his beer, quite contented.

Over at Bluff Court Sir George frowned. He'd heard the shotgun cracks. Damned poachers ... or that Larkin fellow, he shouldn't wonder. He'd had his suspicions for some while. He stepped purposefully towards his wood and heard a rustle. Although he caught a glimpse of two darting figures he couldn't see their faces. Primrose and Victoria raced to Pop's meadow and warned their father that Sir George was on the warpath. Pop deftly hid his gun in the old cart that stood nearby. The girls jumped in too.

Victoria and Primrose were frequent trespassers at Bluff Court.

Pop took wild duck from his neighbour's wood, courtesy of the girls' groundwork.

Sir George Bluff-Gore had his suspicions about Pop Larkin.

Sir George strode over and accused Pop point-blank of shooting but Pop alluded to his bad ear and said he never shot these days. Sir George muttered something about this sort of thing never happening when he had a gamekeeper. Pop took the opportunity to remind him of his offer to buy Bluff Court but Sir George would not be moved. He abominated the idea of his family home being dismantled and demolished for scrap. 'Some of us have a sense of history, Larkin. Good day to you.' Pop watched his plus-foured figure retreating. What a waste, he thought. With Charley's help he could do a lot with the raw materials of the house, make three hundred per cent maybe and still have enough of the necessary to build that bungalow he had in mind for Charley and Mariette.

He walked back to Home Farm. The postman was handing over three thick catalogues to Montgomery - full of wedding dresses and bridesmaids' outfits for Ma and Mariette to pore over. Ma thundered downstairs to inspect them and in her excitement only half heard Pop making some arrangement over the phone. When asked, he explained he was going to see Lady Bluff-Gore and tapped the side of his nose.

'Going up in the world, aren't we?' laughed Ma.

'I do hope so, Ma, I do hope so.'

Ma was preparing a vast batch of pies, flans and tarts and glanced out of the window. Charley was singing as he chopped wood in the yard. She noted that he was filling out a bit and getting quite brown. Pop joined her by the window and looked out proudly. 'Perfick,' he said, watching Mariette come over and give Charley a kiss. His hand strayed to Ma's rump as it so often did in the kitchen and if Ma hadn't been busy he would have suggested a little lie-down.

It struck him as being a little cruel

that Charley and Mariette should still be sleeping in separate rooms but Ma was adamant that she wasn't having unmarried people sleeping together in her house.

'We do.'

'I know, but that's different. We've got children.'

The logic of this defeated even Pop but as he made his way to meet Lady Bluff-Gore he thought again about the possibility of marrying Ma at last, in a double wedding with Charley and Mariette.

'Trouble is, I don't know if George would consider living abroad,' said Lady B-G.

'But think of the swimming pool, the golf course and the beach all over the garden wall.' Pop tapped the advertisement for villas he'd seen in *The Times*. Since Charley had joined the household he'd taken quite a shine to the Thunderer. 'It's a snip, isn't it? El bargain.' Lady Bluff-Gore gave him a conspiratorial wink and then a wide smile as Pop beamed back.

Walking home he mused how important it was that this all went ahead. Charley and Mariette had picked out the spot by the river where they wanted their bungalow built. They spent hours there daydreaming about how their home would be when they were installed, always falling into a passionate embrace when they stepped onto the grass where their bedroom would stand. Mustn't blow this one, thought Pop.

Back home Ma and Mariette were engrossed in their catalogues. At first Pop was too preoccupied to take much interest or notice as they compared bodices and skirts and sleeves and veils and silks and velvets and satins and laces. There wasn't one dress that had absolutely everything perfect. He wandered out into the yard where Charley was heading off towards the woods for a walk, explaining to Pop that he felt able to contribute little to the fashion debate. Then it clicked with Pop. Catalogues. Catalogues! He wasn't having his Mariette married in a mail-order wedding dress! He wasn't having his little girls in mail-order bridesmaid dresses. He wasn't having Ma in some mail-order outsize job. Nothing but the best for them - he'd send them to London to buy from the very best stores. Derry and Toms, Debenhams, Selfridges even. Perfick.

He became aware that Charley was agitated. 'What is it, old man?'

'I'm going to marry your daughter but how am I going to look after her? What are my prospects? I've chucked away my chances with the Inland Revenue. I've a little saved up but that won't go far.'

Pop waved a dismissive hand and said something about all the money Charley had earned with the strawberry lark. He had catalogues on his mind just then. That night in bed with Ma he put his foot down, so to

Up to London for the day: Ma, Mariette and Charley.

speak. 'We're not having no wedding on the cheap. Mariette's going to look like a queen - and you like an empress. I'll meet the price, sell off a bit of surplus. Don't worry about that, Ma. The main thing is to go shopping for the right dresses. Nothing but the best.'

'You're a lovely man, Pop.'

He stroked her tummy, convinced it would be twins again this time, but Ma was doubtful.

'Don't matter, boy or girl, it'll be perfick.'

The Jerebohms lived in a large mansion flat in Victoria. It was slightly overfurnished, just as Pinkie Jerebohm was slightly overweight, usually slightly overdressed and slightly overwrought and her husband, who worked in the city, was grossly overpaid. For some time now they had been thinking of buying a house in the country. It would satisfy their desire to lead a slightly grander social life than the mansion flat allowed and, if they farmed the estate, it would create a handy tax loss for Mr Jerebohm. He liked the idea of riding to hounds and she fancied elegant garden parties and croquet on the lawn.

They hadn't had much luck with brochures sent to them by estate agents, whom Mr Jerebohm pronounced as crooks to a man, and so they decided to do a little field work of their own and poke around their chosen area of Kent one weekend.

Just as the Jerebohms were contemplating their excursion to Kent, Mariette and Ma were boarding the train to London for their shopping spree. At the last minute Charley had decided to go too, to visit his aunt, and in his scramble to find Ma and Mariette's carriage he had almost knocked over Corinne Perigo, also London-bound. A coldly beautiful woman of a certain age, Corinne Perigo and her set were distainful of Pop and all at Home Farm. She ignored Charley's apology.

It was agreed that Charley, Ma and Mariette should rendezvous at tea time at the Marble Arch Hotel. Pop's older brother, Perce, worked there as a waiter so they never had to pay and Ma did love those dainty sandwiches and eclairs, usually eating at least two plates of each.

The girls had an exhausting day, up Oxford Street on the north side and down on the south but finding nothing at all that they liked. It was very dispiriting and only the prospect of tea kept them going.

Charley arrived just as they'd settled down and Uncle Perce kept the group supplied with scones, tea and cakes. Charley had had quite a day. When he reached Aunt Bridget's in Harrow he had told her his news and was just going to pack up some things to take back to the farm when the front door-bell rang. From the living room he could hear the voice of Mr Shell, his old employer. Shell, quite unable to accept Charley's resignation, had made it his business to track him down. He felt personally insulted but, very nobly, wanted to offer Charley a second chance.

Unable to stall any longer, Aunt Bridget had led Shell into her small suburban sitting room where the French windows to the garden stood open. Charley had scarpered across the garden and over the hedge. As he explained all this he picked twigs from his jacket; Mariette held his hand and Ma laughed like a jelly.

Uncle Perce came over to speak for a moment - the image of Pop, but greyer and more sinewy. Charley was introduced and Ma lamented their frustrating morning at the shops. He roared with laughter. 'You don't want no wedding gear from shops. You want it specially made!'

'Like royalty, you mean?' asked Mariette.

'Exactly,' replied Uncle Perce. He explained that he had an, um, er ... friend who also worked at the hotel, as a housekeeper. She was a Russian countess who had been reduced to such work but who was an expert needlewoman. She'd made clothes for all the toffs, including some members of the Royal Family although she was too discreet to divulge names. Perce would fix it, he promised - introductions, then the designs,

Uncle Percy

Percy Larkin was ten years older than Pop but looked more or less the same age, which boded well for Pop as he got older, Ma thought. He worked these days at the Marble Arch Hotel, in London, as a room-service waiter. His network of friends and fellow staffers at the hotel ensured that Ma never paid for tea when she went there - as she always did when in London.

The brothers didn't see a lot of each other, but were intensely fond of one another and loyal. Perce had never married - he didn't think it would be fair to all his girlfriends - but he'd come as near as dammit with the Countess. She was a beautiful Russian who, as a girl, had fled to Paris after the Revolution. Impoverished, with only exquisite dressmaking skills to support her, she ultimately arrived in London and worked as a housekeeper at the Marble Arch Hotel. Very occasionally and very discreetly, she designed and made clothes for aristocratic clients. It was she who created Mariette's wedding dress.

Perce really came up trumps for Pop when he arrived for the wedding. It was Pop's morning in court, defending himself against Pinkie Jerebohm's charge of indecent assault and things were going badly for him, with Corinne Perigo lying through her teeth in the stand. Perce recognised her as someone who used a different name and went in for afternoon room service at the Marble Arch Hotel ... hardly someone to testify on morals. The case against Pop collapsed.

Uncle Perce could take or leave the countryside - and leave it he invariably did, with a sense of relief. His idea of country air was a good fug around the hearth of the Hare and Hounds while waiting for his train back to London, but he was a devoted brother and uncle nonetheless, never forgetting a birthday or anniversary and always willing to open doors or to grease any wheels where he could in town.

fittings, the lot. He checked his watch. 'Got to get back now. I'm on duty, see, and you'd be surprised how many people want room service in the afternoons, if you know what I mean. Quite shameless, some of them. Open the door in the altogether with madam lounging in bed wearing nothing but a smile like a Cheshire cat!' They all laughed as his wiry figure scurried off.

Whilst Mr Jerebohm was negotiating a rate for the best room at the Hare and Hounds, Pop, Edith and the Brigadier were downstairs in the bar. 'Even by your standards, Larkin, you look like a dog with two tails.'

Pop smirked. His ruse with Mary Bluff-Gore had worked like a dream. She'd stressed how if they sold up they could afford a gardener for the winter months, mentioned that good wine in Spain cost only pennies a bottle, and reminded Sir George that on their last stay in a warm climate she'd been too warm at night to wear her ... That did it and Sir George and Pop had shaken on the deal earlier that day.

The conversation turned to preparations for the wedding, Pop reminding Edith and the Brigadier that they were amongst the most honoured guests. Pop saw the Jerebohms talking to Jim, the landlord, from the corner of his eye and cocked his ear. The bloke seemed to be asking him about houses ... The Brigadier was well stuck into some old campaigner's story when Edith noticed Pop was distracted.

'You naughty man. You weren't listening to the Brigadier's perfectly ghastly story. You're eavesdropping, aren't you? Up to something.'

'When do I ever get up to anything, Edith?' said Pop. 'Now would you two excuse me for a few moments ...' He headed towards the bar.

The next evening Pop, with Charley and Mariette, was looking at Bluff Court and its ill-tended grounds from over the fence. He explained that he'd closed the deal at seven thousand pounds, securing it with a cash deposit. He waved an arm towards the house. 'That's where the makings of your bungalow will come from.' Mariette was ecstatic, but Charley frowned. He was worried that Pop had over-stretched himself. 'What about the rest of the money Pop? You're talking about thousands of pounds.'

Pop led them to one of the outbuildings and unlocked the padlock. 'Thousands we need, thousands we've got.' He pointed to stacks of packing cases. 'Army surplus. Tons of it. Greatcoats, boots, blankets ... chap in Maidstone wants them for the Nigerian Army. This, plus the copper wiring from the minesweeper in the other shed ...'

'You're an amazing man, Pop.' Charley accepted the cigar his father-in-law-to-be offered, although he didn't smoke and he and Mariette went off towards the meadow. Pop watched them fondly as they faded into the dusk, lit his own cigar and tossed the match away ...

The dusky shapes of Charley and Mariette had married with the night. Lord knows how long they'd walked or how far, lost as they were in the scented darkness of the wood. Charley turned and saw a great glow.

'Look, Mariette. Its the most amazing sunset. Over there.' He waved an arm. Mariette had known every track in these woods since babyhood. When she saw the glow that Charley pointed towards she knew it was no sunset. It was east. It was home! She grabbed his hand and made him run with her. When they got to the farm she wept with relief to see Ma and Pop standing in the yard and the sleepy, puzzled children huddling round the front door. But Pop's face was grim as he watched the last of the flames lick up the remains of his outhouse. She caught a glimpse of the back end of a departing fire engine in the track.

'Shot myself in the foot there, good and proper. I could have sworn that match was out ...' Pop was trying hard to be philosophical and jolly. Mariette thought, that's the end of our bungalow, and hated herself for it. Charley, too, said the wrong thing. 'You can't buy Bluff Court now.' Pop didn't really hear. He was trying so hard not to cry. Ma decided the only solution was a great big supper - sausages and chips and lots of ketchup. She strode into the kitchen and set to.

There was a family conference at the table. Charley suggested borrowing the money for Bluff Court, getting a mortgage, but Ma was horrified. The Larkins had never borrowed from anyone. Pop, though, was prepared to try anything and allowed Mariette to persuade him. 'Let Charley try, Pop. He's ever so clever at things like this.'

It was a great pity that the next day, when Charley had to go looking for a mortgage, was the day of the cricket match. Mariette kissed Charley off in that old suit of his and had all his cricket gear clean and ready for his return.

It went well for a while. Charley told the bank manager that his father-in-law-to-be was a farmer; the man agreed that the purchase of Bluff Court was a shrewd investment. 'I only have to pick up the phone. They're usually guided by any recommendation I make.'

'Perfick,' said Charley. 'I mean perfect.'

'And what's your father-in-law's name?'

'Syd Larkin.'

The bank manager's face went white. He slowly tore the form that Charley had so painstakingly completed into shreds. Then he showed him the door.

The children had never seen Pop despondent like this. He was sitting on a pile of scorched logs and watching

Pinkie Jerebohm

Pinkie Jerebohm wasn't an evil woman: she was simply rather stupid. Plump and fluffy, obsessed with her weight and permanently on a diet, self-absorbed yet devoted to her husband, Pinkie had a very constricted view of the world. In her naiveté she imagined that all she and Sunbeam - as she insisted on calling her husband - needed to do to slip into rural society was to buy a big house and the right clothes. Lazy, indolent and snobbish, Pinkie was keen to have a large local staff to clean up after her - the country, after all, was so dirty.

Pinkie had been spoilt throughout her marriage and was easily flattered. She liked to imagine herself as some latter-day Lady Muck, riding to hounds, gently tending her roses, holding scintillating evenings for the cream of the county and bestowing largesse upon a grateful and adoring peasantry. In fact she was much more at home in the overstuffed opulence of their London mansion flat where - just as Pinkie invariably wore one piece of jewellery too many - there was always one expensive knick-knack too many on every surface.

Weakness and vanity were Pinkie's downfall. She was susceptible to the malign influence of the scorned Corinne Perigo and only too ready to believe that Pop had made a pass at her - so she tried to defend her honour in court. Pop had encountered more formidable adversaries in the cowshed. She didn't stand a chance. Her flirtation with country life came to an abrupt close and the Jerebohms returned to London considerably poorer but, sadly, not very much wiser.

Deep down Pinkie had a kind heart and if she had given things time, contained her social pretensions and not underestimated her neighbours, it all might have turned out better. As it was, the most she and Sunbeam could salvage from their stay at Bluff Court was a fund of gruesome stories with which to bore their few friends in London at stiff little dinner parties.

Family support for Pop and Montgomery at the cricket match.

them play in the ashes, hands black from their games. They called out about things they'd found in the pyre and Pop tried to respond but nothing could cheer him. He kicked up a cloud of ash and was only roused by the sound of Angela Snow's car as she screeched into the yard. The dear girl ran over to Pop and held him in a warm, scented hug.

'Just one of those things,' muttered Pop. Angela asked if she could do anything. Pop told her ruefully that there wasn't any insurance to claim on and that the only thing to do was to have a good stiff drink. For once Angela declined. She was taking the Brigadier shopping for a Panama hat. Pop had almost forgotten the cricket match ... his spirit seemed to have totally evaporated.

'There is one thing you might do for me Angela, since you're such a toff. There's a couple staying at the Hare and Hounds. She calls him Sunbeam and he calls her Pinkie. Down here looking for a country house. See what you can do, would you?'

'Scream,' roared Angela Snow. She got the picture right away and Pop tiredly waved her off. He braced himself. The cricket match, of course.

Pop was given out by Sir George - unfairly he thought.

Mustn't give in to these little setbacks. Had to wave the flag. Monty batting. Must get there.

The parish was playing a nearby village's eleven. Pop, in his whites, was facing some fast bowling, the Vicar at the other end of the wicket. He knew his concentration wasn't all it might be but he was trying his best. The Brigadier and Sir George were umpiring. At the edge of the field Montgomery was already padded up as he was next in and Edith was fussing around with the tea things. A few spectators lounged in deckchairs around the edge of the pitch. Pop rather hoped that this match, usually an annual riot, would distract him. He knew that Ma and Mariette, together with darling Angela Snow, were there to wish him well.

He was one short of his fifty, and beginning to feel rather more cheerful, when he was bowled a wicked googlie. The enemy wicket-keeper shrieked for an appeal, Ma shrieked back. Never touched it, she cried, and Pop was defiant on the field. He knew that a gentleman walked, and hadn't the General told him that he was a

Edith bellowed encouragement from the tea stand.

Montgomery sets off to do a spot of match-saving.

gentleman, but this was a bit much. Sir George raised a finger, almost wagged it, as Pop paused. And then he walked. It was a day of defeats. Hates me for buying his hutch, Pop thought, as he retired. He met Monty on the way back from the wicket and they exchanged a knowing glance. Pop sat back to watch his son, just a little boy, really.

As Monty played himself in, Angela Snow lounged in her deckchair and extolled the pleasures of country life to the Jerebohms. She told them all about Bluff Court, said it was the finest house in the county and that this village was the prettiest for miles. When they asked about Pop, Angela praised him to the skies. 'He can put his leg before my wicket anytime he likes.'

'Oh really,' said the Jerebohms as one. Neither of them had the faintest idea about cricket terminology, or wildlife, or architecture or anything. But they did think that Angela had class and must know what she was talking about. Corinne Perigo was seated near them and gave Pop a baleful moue as she commiserated with the decision to declare him out. She

Pop was usually on for a harmless flirt but he drew the line at Corinne Perigo.

sympathised about the fire, too, and offered any help she could. Pop was almost touched until he saw again that predatory look in her eye. He walked away and told her he hoped she'd enjoy the rest of the match. Pinkie Jerebohm, who had witnessed and half-heard some of this was greatly reassured. These simple country people knew their place and didn't try to mix with their betters. Respectful, yes, and detached in their humble way. She felt quietly confident that life in the village could be just so.

Angela winked at Pop as he moved away.

Pop had more important matters to concern him. There was Monty on the pitch, batting like a hero. Pop's heart almost burst with pride when the boy staved off the hostile bowling and played a fine little innings that as good as saved the match.

Angela was doing a magnificent job of selling Bluff Court to the Jerebohms. Pop was unbuckling his pads and trying to deflect an unwelcome interruption from Corinne Perigo when she hurried up to him and whispered something that made him smile at last. He excused himself stiffly from Corinne Perigo and hurried off to the car park, still in his whites. His Rolls arrived outside Bluff Court just moments before the Jerebohms arrived in theirs. Pinkie was slightly dismayed to see such a common little man with such a noble car. Probably stole it, she

The Jerebohms were raced around Bluff Court so that Pop could return to the match.

thought to herself.

Pop was anxious to show the Jerebohms the house and grounds quickly, so that he could get back to the cricket match, he said. He lead them into the great hall with its beamed ceiling and massive fireplace. He showed them the library and dining room with their linen-fold panelling, the great stained-glass window on the landing, the cool, dark kitchens, the fifteen or so bedrooms with their magnificent views. On a clear winter's day, Pop said in a moment of inspiration, you could see the sea. Mr Jerebohm looked doubtful.

Then he showed them the grounds, a bit overgrown at the moment, Pop agreed, but nothing that a man and a lad couldn't fix in a few days. This prompted Pinkie to equire about the availability of local help. No problem, said Pop, crossing his fingers behind his back. They saw the pool, the lake, the greenhouses.

'Everything grows hell for leather. Cherries, strawberries, hops, apples, corn. Everything. Not called the garden of England for nothing,' he enthused.

Jerebohm was suspicious. Why do you want to sell it if you're waxing so lyrical?' Pop thought for a second and explained it was sentiment, he supposed. If he didn't sell it to a couple like themselves he would be forced to sell it piecemeal for scrap. Didn't really want to do that, but ... He went on to tell Mr Jerebohm that he should stock the woods with pheasant and the lake with wild duck - a wise afterthought as Jerebohm was very keen to shoot. The couple moved away for a private chat and Jerebohm came back to offer Pop twelve thousand pounds.

Pop snorted. He could get a thousand for the stained glass alone, let alone the marble, the panelling and so on. Eventually after a couple of rounds Pop settled for seventeen thousand, with five thousand in readies as soon as the banks had opened next day. Pinkie was ecstatic. She was already dreaming of croquet parties and tennis weekends.

Pop returned to the cricket match in a much better mood, just in time to see Charley clean bowled. He clapped him on the shoulder. 'Cheer up, Charley boy. Tail-end duck ain't the end of the world'.

'It's not only the duck, Pop. We didn't get the mortgage. You can't buy Bluff Court.'

Pop chuckled. 'Can't buy it old man? I've just sold it.'

Next day, as soon as he had the money safe in his duffel, bag Pop drove over to Bluff Court and handed it over to a disbelieving Sir George. Lady Mary appeared from the kitchens, looking very pleased.

'Five thousand. The balance. Ties up our little transaction.'

'Absolutely. Forfeit your deposit if you hadn't turned up.'

Pop asked for the duffel bag back. Primrose would not have been best pleased if he'd left it at Bluff Court and Sir George handed it back before going to telephone his solicitor. Lady Mary tipped her chin towards the garden and Pop followed her outside. He gave her a wad of notes. Five per cent 'commission' in cash and as she stuffed them in her pockets Sir George came outside.

'That's all settled then,' he allowed himself a smile.

'Perfick,' said Pop. As he headed to the truck the Jerebohms' Rolls purred through the gates and up the drive towards Bluff Court. 'What the blazes..! Who the hell do they think they are?'

'That's the Jerebohms. The new owners,' Pop explained.

Mariette's wedding dress, Ma's and all the bridesmaids' frocks were made by Uncle Percy's friend, the Countess.

EPISODE 4

When the Green Woods Laugh

PART TWO

Pinkie Jerebohm was taking country life seriously. In some way she thought it would help her to lose weight. She little realised that every time she thumped through the bluebell woods she disturbed a brace or two of pheasant that Pop most obligingly shot when they flew over his land. One morning, over breakfast, Pinkie was considering her social launch, her season as it were, and suggested to her husband that they should start off with a getting-to-know-you dinner party for the neighbours. Mr Jerebohm weakly assented. He wasn't finding country life quite as thrilling as his wife was. For a start it was so noisy, with all those animals calling at each other, the crack of shotguns - every Johnny down here seemed to be able bag birds except him - and then there was the staff problem. Contrary to what that Larkin fellow had said, they'd found it impossible to hire locally. They were just about managing with a half-witted Austrian girl called Ingrid. A dinner party? All right, he supposed so, and returned to the financial pages.

Ma and Pop Larkin were having a glass of beer before lunch and discussing their new neighbours. Pop was willing to make allowances for anyone whom he'd fleeced as soundly as the Jerebohms and told Ma that Pinkie was all right if a bit excitable and overly sentimental about matters

Charley and Mariette leave church on Sunday morning.

Corinne Perigo was a dangerous woman, but even Pop had to concede that she sat well on a horse.

bucolic and that the master was what he called a Piccadilly farmer - saw everything from peapods to pheasants in terms of tax losses.

Charley and Mariette had gone to church, in anticipation of their marriage, but Pop was dismissive. He waved his arm towards his beloved wood and the meadows and asserted that all this was his church and no one could worship more devoutly than he. Ma carried on peeling potatoes and looked at him fondly.

After church, where their banns had been called, Charley and Mariette went to sit outside the Hare and Hounds with Edith Pilchester and the Brigadier. Captain and Corinne Perigo clipped past in immaculate riding kit and graced the little group with a nod. Corinne gave Charley an admiring glance.

The young ones headed off home to lunch. Ma was interested to hear that Mrs Perigo was back with the Captain. She reminisced about all the other fellows that Mrs Perigo had trifled with - a vet, a naval officer, an agricultural inspector ... a girl with a hearty appetite, Ma said, ladling out gravy for the chicken. All came to sticky ends of one sort or another, she mused darkly.

Primrose, who sat next to Charley at lunch and stared adoringly at him, found this most upsetting. Washing up later with the twins and Mongomery she announced that she would never run off with someone. How could you, if you loved someone? She just didn't understand and was going to ask Ma to explain but Pop and Ma had retired upstairs for a little lie-down, so she was left with her bafflement. Charley, observing Ma and Pop's exit, had taken Mariette's hand, kissed her fingers and told her that he intended to make her every bit as happy as Pop made Ma.

Pinkie Jerebohm called round a bit later and surveyed the yard of Home Farm with some distaste. She'd never seen such mess and clutter. And all those half-naked children making such a racket. She asked Victoria if Mrs Larkin was at home. Yes, she was, explained Victoria, but she was resting. Pregnant you see. And Mr Larkin? He was resting too, said Victoria. It dawned on Pinkie what sort of rest the Larkins might be having, so she left a note about the dinner party and asked Victoria to hand it on. Primrose and Victoria giggled as she drove away, discomfited and embarrassed.

Charley and Mariette had gone to visit the Brigadier, taking with them a large piece of Ma's ham. They found him dozing in his garden, dressed in shabby whites, the crumbs of a meagre lunch at his side. They'd come to ask a favour. 'We'd like you to be best man at our wedding,' mumbled Charley. Demurring at first, but deeply touched, the Brigadier finally agreed. His only worry, he thought, as Charley and Mariette departed, was how on earth would he afford the regulation kit?

It started off as a little anxiety but became a huge one. When he muttered something about it to Pop some while later, Pop tried to fob him off with some nonsense about it being an old Kentish custom for the father of the bride to provide these things, but the Brigadier was having none of this. No. The only honourable thing to do was to retire and allow Charley to give the job to a younger, less impoverished man. It was very sad, but it just wasn't on.

On the night of the Jerebohms' dinner party, Ma and Pop made a bit of an effort. Ma wore her mink stole - bought with last year's strawberry money - and Pop polished the Rolls. Although it was mid-summer, it was chilly in Bluff Court. Pop noticed that damp birch had been put in the fire-place; and it smoked cheerlessly. Little thimbles of sherry were passed around by Ingrid and conversation between the Larkins, the Perigos and the Jerebohms was stilted. Pinkie, shivering in a tightly corseted oyster satin number, tried her best while Sunbeam jabbed moodily at the fire with a long poker. Ah, country life, she thought to herself when they moved into the dining room for dinner. So real, so unpretentious, so simple.

Pop found himself seated next to Corinne Perigo. It was odd. She was a damn fine-looking woman and she had that look in her eye, but for once Pop was repelled, not enchanted. Tries too hard, he thought to himself as she

Corinne Perigo

Corinne Perigo was undoubtedly a fine-looking woman if you went for the haughty type and didn't mind a bit too much make-up. She sat very well on a horse and was an aggressive rider to hounds. She considered herself several cuts above the Larkin family and barely acknowledged them, in fact, if she met them in the village or in the lanes. She felt much more comfortable with the weekend country dwellers who gave Sunday lunches for friends down from London, or at cocktail parties and the cultural soirées that revolved around a little group of intellectuals in Canterbury.

What she liked most of all, though, was spending time with men, preferably not her husband. She was reputedly responsible for the downfall of a vet, a naval officer and a man from the forestry commission - and that was just in the past two years. Most recently she had been going to London to spend afternoons in the Marble Arch Hotel with a Mr Fanshaw. Yes, Corinne Perigo wanted it both ways - the status of the wife and the pleasures of the mistress.

Despite regarding Pop Larkin as a common little man, Corinne Perigo also wanted to become better acquainted with him. She wasn't ashamed - a lot of her girlfriends in London spoke of the charms of a 'bit of rough' and a spot of rough and tumble with Pop was most appealing. It was when Pop continued to spurn her seductive advances that she turned really nasty and encouraged that silly Pinkie Jerebohm to take Pop to court.

It was her mistake: what remained of her tattered reputation was ruined and she had to start frequenting a different hotel.

knocked her knee against his and later invited him to retrieve her deliberately dropped napkin from the floor beside her silky ankle. He looked across to Ma, whose dismay was clear. It wasn't about Corinne, but the tiny portion of prawn cocktail in front of her. This was followed by a small piece of beef carved with elaborate flourish by Mr Jerebohm.

Ingrid served the vegetables and Pop gave her one of his show-stopping smiles. The poor girl relaxed and gave Pop an an extra spoonful. Corinne Perigo glared at her and started to feel distinctly hostile towards Pop. How dare he resist her, common little man? It was years since anyone had scorned her like this.

Pop's glass was empty. Ingrid looked at Mr Jerebohm, who nodded, and Pop's glass was filled. He raised it.

'Friend of mine is a wine-shipper in the city. Greek,' Mr Jerebohm informed his guests.

Pop thought the wine was barely good enough for stripping paint, Greek or not, but drank it manfully and reminded Mr Jerebohm that he'd soon be delivering the skiff that came with the house. Had to take it to Home Farm for safe keeping when the Court was empty. Corinne placed a hand on his arm. 'Will you be hunting this year?' Pop nodded. 'We could share a stirrup cup,' she purred, in a final attempt to woo him. Pop shrugged and tried to catch what Jerebohm was saying about his pheasants. Despite Pop's restocking, he lamented, he'd barely seen a bird. Pop muttered something about poachers and how you couldn't be too careful. Ma gaily said that they had dozens hanging at home and she'd send a brace over. Pop shot her a look. 'Last years' in the freezer, of course,' he explained to Jerebohm.

The excruciating evening wore on. 'Good heavens. Half-past ten already. We'd better be off, Ma,' announced Pop as soon as it was decent. Back home, Ma still clutching her mink, made bacon and eggs and tipped large measures of Johnny Walker into their tea. 'Don't know when I'll ever warm up,' she said.

'How about a nice hot bath, Ma. All steamy and bubbling. We could take a bottle of champagne up. Why not?' suggested Pa. They finished off their eggs and bacon and fried bread and retired.

Downstairs Mariette and Charley were planning their bungalow. 'What to you think, Charley? One bathroom or two?' Charley heard the splashing noises and the laughter and the pop of the champagne cork and Ma's shriek. 'One should do us fine, don't you think?'

Good as his word, Pop was getting the skiff ready to return to Bluff Court. Montgomery was helping. Pop took a long draught of beer that had been cooling in the lake and watched

The Brigadier

The Brigadier had seen better days. He was living now with his unmarried sister in a cramped and shabby cottage just up the lane from Home Farm, but he often reminisced about the years before the war when he cut a dash as a subaltern in India. His days in Simla - running affairs with two married women at once, playing polo and poker in the cool, green hill station - were charmed.

Now he lived on a tiny pension; his clothes were darned and darned again. Sometimes his shoes were laced with string and his summer whites were always crumpled. But the Brigadier's bearing was still distinguished and his command of Latin impeccable. He still had an eye for the ladies, too, particularly Angela Snow, with whom he once spent a quite thrilling afternoon. A pity he had drunk too much champagne to remember anything about it afterwards.

The Brigadier was a gentleman himself, and could always recognise another, which was why he and Pop Larkin were such good friends and respected each other. Pop aways called him General, which he didn't actually mind. The Brigadier was best man at the wedding of Mariette and Charley and it almost moved him to tears to be embraced by the Larkin family like that.

When alone the Brigadier ate and drank frugally, but he could always be persuaded to accept a large snifter from Pop, whether or not the sun was over the yard-arm, and was often tempted by Ma's cooking. Sunday lunch under the walnut tree was often the highlight of his week. Although he was still a member of two London clubs whose subscriptions he could ill-afford, the Brigadier went to town less and less.

The Larkin children adored him - regarding him almost like a grandparent - and he had an especially soft spot for Mariette. One day, when she and Charley start a family, he'll probably find himself a godfather.

Charley and Mariette playing house on the plot where the bungalow was to be built, moving from invisible room to room and pretending to have breakfast. His reverie was broken by the arrival of Angela Snow and the Brigadier. Taking Pop aside, Angela explained that Arthur (as she now called him), was in a terrible state about being best man, awfully worried about the expense. He was, she warned, about to withdraw. The old chap was sitting under the walnut tree with Ma, eating a decent lunch, and Angela and Pop joined them, a plot by now hatched between them.

After lunch Angela offered to loan the Brigadier the money to hire the neccessary from Moss Bros, but this gave the Brigadier a better idea. Once back home, he went to his old military chest and lifted out his carefully packed uniform. Slightly mothy but still exquisitely cut from the finest cloth. He held the tunic in front of himself. Might just do, he thought, sucking in his stomach. Angela, who was still with him, agreed. He would look quite spendid. There wasn't a man in the county to touch him. Problem solved, the Brigadier took Angela's arm and led her out to his garden.

'Calls for some champagne, don't you think, Arthur?' Angela thought there might be a dusty bottle or two in the off-licence next to the Hare and Hounds and was back in less than five minutes.

Angela and the Brigadier spent an agreeable afternoon drinking champagne, listening to some of his old 78 rpm records on the radiogram and dancing. She was a girl in a million, the Brigadier thought. Awfully good-looking in that rangy, blonde, well-bred way, a bit like a racehorse. Same marvellous legs, and such spirit. Wonderful to know they still made girls like this, he thought as Angela opened the second bottle of Bollinger. Good sport, good fun, good heart. Jolly good figure, too, he thought as they danced to an old Henry Hall foxtrot. Angela's long, tawny arms were wrapped around him and she was whispering something. Damned shame he couldn't quite hear. Something about upstairs. They stumbled into the dim hallway of his cottage and propped each other up as they climbed towards his bedroom. Sadly, that is the last thing that the Brigadier would ever remember of this magical afternoon, for when he awoke he was rumpled and nicely dishevelled, fully clothed, except for his shoes, but Angela Snow was gone. Well, you never knew, he thought to himself. Marvellous girl ...

Pop was ready to take the skiff back to Bluff Court. Montgomery was saddened but Pop half promised to buy another one and this consoled Montgomery. He pulled away from the bank, pleased to have some time to himself. Ma and Mariette were at the Marble Arch Hotel for another of their

Ma and Mariette on their way to London for a shopping spree and dress fittings.

fittings with that Countess and all he had to do was deliver the skiff and meet them at the station later.

Pinkie Jerebohm was a teensy bit anxious. She had Corinne Perigo coming over for tea at four and she wanted it to be just so. She was relieved to see Pop approach in the skiff - it would have been a bit shaming if he'd arrived when Corinne was there. She met him at the jetty.

'Ahoy there! Perfick day, Mrs Jerebohm.' Pop looked around the lake and gave the boat an affectionate glance. 'Shame to waste an afternoon like this. I'd love to take her out for one last row around the lake. What do you think?' Pinkie was flustered, as usual. Larkin was such a charmer, and a short skim across the lake would be fun, but, would there be time? Pop assured her that he'd get her back in time for tea and they set off despite Pinkie's nerves. She couldn't swim, she explained to Pop.He reassured her that she was in no danger and that the best place to pick those wild orchids she wanted was on the other side of the lake.

He moored the boat and helped Pinkie out, sniffing the fragrant air. 'Wild flowers, you want? You got them all here. Poppies, cornflowers, herb robert, speedwell, those orchids you like, woodbine, thistle. There ain't nothing more perfick than wild summer flowers in England.' Pinkie, too, was intoxicated by the mossy quiet

Pop takes Pinkie for a little row arond the lake at Bluff Court.

of the wood, with glints from the lake sparkling through gaps in the trees. She accepted a posy from Pop and ran about, almost skittishly, looking for other flowers. Pop leaned against a tree and contentedly observed her. Her bosoms wobbled very prettily too as she dashed from flower to flower. Pop had never objected to a spot of avoir-du-poids on his women.

He was just thinking that he might give her a bit of a cuddle when Pinkie

The intoxicating scents of the wild flowers began to give Pop a few ideas.

noticed the time. Lord, it was gone half-past four. They must get back right away. Resignedly Pop agreed and they returned to the boat to row across the lake. Pinkie was agitated. She could see Corinne Perigo near the jetty and it was just too mortifying to have kept her waiting like this. As they approached the jetty she tried to get up but Pop told her to stay still. The lake was at its deepest just there and he wanted to keep the skiff steady as they moored. Pinkie ignored him and stood, waving at Corinne. The boat rocked alarmingly and Pinkie lost her balance. Only Pop, standing to steady her, saved her from a dip in the lake and he finally managed to moor the boat.

By now Pinkie was almost hysterical. She'd screamed in terror when she thought she would fall in the water and now, with Pop's arms around her, she screamed on. Corinne rushed up and started going on about being a witness.

Pop had liked the idea of giving Pinkie a friendly squeeze, but not under these circumstances.

'You absolute swine," she hissed at Pop.' I saw you grab her just now. You're not going to get away with this.' She turned to Pinkie. 'You must report him. I'm your witness. Have him charged.'

Pinkie didn't know what to think. 'I was startled, that's all. I don't think ...'

'Tell the police, Pinkie.' Corinne Perigo led her by the elbow. Pop shrugged and walked away, pondering on the strangeness of women and wondering why they couldn't all be like Ma.

The vicar, Mr Spinks, came over to Home Farm a few days later to finalise details of the wedding. Which hymns, whether or not Mariette was going to promise to obey Charley and whether or not Pop was ever going to marry Ma. Pop said that it didn't make sense from a tax point of view, so they'd decided to wait for a while. The vicar looked pained. Then Sergeant Wilson from the local police station cycled up the track and very apologetically handed Pop a summons. Pop opened it and began to read out loud.

'... hereby charged that on the said date you did unlawfully and against her wishes attempt to interfere with ...'

The vicar looked bewildered, Mariette said is was just ridiculous and Ma exploded with rage. Pop read on and saw that he was summoned to appear in court on the very morning of the wedding.

Sergeant Wilson shook his head. 'You can't do that Syd. I hate to do this. Get a good lawyer, that's my advice.'

Pop snorted. He'd defend himself. Charley had the brains in the family; he'd help him to prepare a defence. Mariette was in tears by now and even Pop's outraged confidence was shattered somewhat when Wilson told him that the magistrate who would hear the case was Sir George Bluff-Gore.

On the morning of the wedding Pop dressed carefully and went with Charley, also in morning dress, to the court building. Charley gave some last-minute coaching to Pop as they waited for his case to be called. 'Don't forget ... 'I put it to you...with the greatest respect ... my learned friend' ... remember to pause to throw the enemy witnesses off balance ... make sure you call Sir George "Your Honour". ' Pop nodded grimly. It was now well after ten o'clock now and the wedding was at twelve.

Ma was sitting in the public gallery, massive and magnificent in her lilac wedding outfit. The Jerebohms and the Perigos were also in court. Edith Pilchester shook her head with scorn as the charge was read out. Pop pleaded not guilty and informed the court that he was defending himself. The prosecuting solicitor, Mr Barlow, then proceeded to present all the facts of the case in question.

Uncle Percy brought the Countess with him for the wedding.

Pinkie was not impressive in the stand and by the end of his cross-examination of her Pop was quietly confident. He'd established that she was terrified of water, couldn't swim and had held on to him for balance at the jetty. Corinne Perigo, though, was another matter. Under oath she swore that she'd seen Pop attempting to molest Pinkie in the boat and things looked bad for Pop. There was a slight disturbance as Uncle Perce and the Countess entered the public gallery. They had just been collected from the station. Perce instantly recognised Mrs Perigo as one of his afternoon room-service regulars, and she certainly didn't call herself Corinne Perigo at the Marble Arch Hotel. He got a message to this effect down to Pop, who called for, and was reluctantly granted, a recess.

Pop took in the news. With Perce as a witness Corinne could be proved to be a liar and to be someone of highly questionable morals at the very least. The case against him would collapse. Corinne Perigo, recognising Uncle Perce in the lobby of the court, tried to persuade Pop to make a deal – back in the box she would say it had all been a

Mariette had had a long wait before Pop arrived home to take her to the church ...

dreadful mistake and that neither she nor Pinkie wanted to see Pop sent down. He would have none of it and called Uncle Perce as his next witness. Corinne's reputation and evidence were duly demolished, Pinkie slumped forward in a faint and the case against Pop was dismissed. There was wild cheering in the court.

Pop drove home in the lorry and honked the horn outside the house. Mariette stepped out, a cloud, a vision, a dream in white satin and lace. Pop stared at her, a lump in his throat. 'My God, you're perfickly beautiful.' She took his arm. 'This is the day when everything's perfick,' Pop went on.

They raced through the lanes to the church and at last the organist could start to play the Wedding March as Pop proudly walked Mariette up the aisle.

... and Charley had had an equally tense time, but the luck of the Larkins triumphed.

The procession at Ville de Fougères approaches the cathedral.

EPISODE 5

A Breath of French Air

PART ONE

Pop Larkin was a worried man. Mariette and Charley had been married for nearly a year and there was still no sign of a little stranger. Wasn't natural, he figured, and hoped that nothing was wrong. Ma had given birth to little Oscar a few months ago and he thought that if Mariette provided a playmate for him it would be just perfick.

That summer, though, everyone seemed a bit out of sorts. The weather had been foul - cold, rainy and windy. They'd hardly sat out in the garden at all. Pop reckoned it was time to shift those tins of pickled gherkins that had been cluttering up the rebuilt barn. Some had started to rust and blow, so he and Charley were off to sell them at auction. Pop explained that when the lot came up Charley was to pretend to be a caterer who'd got wind of a bargain and push the bidding up. Meanwhile Mariette and Ma were trying to amuse themselves on the rain-swept front in Ramsgate. Ma was hugely amused by the fortune-teller's prediction of a journey in store and reckoned it was the drive back to Home Farm in time to cook supper. Mariette was less easily cheered. She just wished Pop would get around to the bungalow. Much as she loved her parents she wished she and Charley could have a place of their own.

In the auction rooms lots of tinned salmon and vintage wines were being bidded for by managers of holiday camps and hotels. Pop pointed them out to Charley. They were the chaps who'd probably be after his pickled gherkins, he whispered confidently. Bidding was slow at first when the lot came up. Pop had reckoned on clearing three hundred, but even with two other bidders as well as Charley, the highest bid seemed to be ninety-five. And, he realised with horror, this had been bid by Charley. A wave of relief flooded over him when someone else took it to a hundred. At least they would be off his hands, but then Charley blew it and bid a hundred and five. That was it. Sold to the gentleman in the third row and Pop's pickled gherkins were shortly reloaded onto the truck on their way back to Home Farm.

Through the black cloud of his bleak mood Pop heard Ma and Mariette describe their afternoon. They'd been caught in the rain on the front but the handsome skipper of a French fishing boat had taken pity and invited them aboard to keep dry. Charley bristled with proprietorial jealousy. The skipper, Ma said, had told them that they should go to Brittany for some sunshine. If they wanted to have any summer at all they'd have to go there. Ma recounted how charming Gérard Brisson had been, how he'd only reluctantly accepted any money for the dozen red mullet she and Mariette had brought back with them, how she rather fancied a trip to France if all Frenchmen were like that.

For once the weather was dreadful. The Larkin family started thinking they needed a change from Kent.

Pa was barely listening, furious with Charley for screwing up the sale, taking bends on the lanes at a lunatic speed and muttering under his breath about disaster and ruin. 'Give it a rest, will you. At least you've still got the gherkins,' said Ma soothingly.

'Yeah. Perfick. We still got 'em.'

Charley didn't make things any easier by reminding Pop that he owed him the hundred and five pounds. Pop glared and said he'd have to wait for it. Ma, hoping to defuse the situation, said never mind, they'd got a nice fish supper to look forward to.

Back home even a massive, treble-strength cocktail couldn't raise Pop's spirits. He clutched and stared gloomily at Ma as she gutted fish for their supper. Outside the rain was bucketing down, the children, restless from being cooped up, were fractious. Only Oscar, with jam all over his face and a little moat of bread and butter all round his high chair, seemed contented. 'We need a holiday. Brittany. We've got to go,' said Ma as she beheaded another mullet.

'Gawd Almighty Ma, what's got into you?'

'This.' Ma waved towards the rain-spattered window with her knife. As if on cue Primrose and Victoria started talking about what their French mistress had told them about Brittany and Mariette produced some brochures she'd picked up from a travel agent on the way back to the truck that afternoon. Pop, rightly, sensed that mutiny was in the air.

Ma continued calmly. She'd been thinking, she said. 'There's not a lot of time left, the kids can go back to school a week late but no later. If we're going to France it's now or never.' Pop felt helpless and looked for support from Charley but he was disappointed. Charley thought Brittany was an excellent idea. He'd spent holidays there with his family before the war and remembered it as a golden place at a golden time. He even remembered the name of the hotel where they used to stay, the Beau Rivage at St-Pierre-le-Port. He continued waxing lyrical about the air, the weather, the beaches and a little train that ran along the coast ...

But the thought of Ma in a bikini did wonders for Pop's mood. 'All right. Suppose we did *allez* for a jolly old promenade *à bientôt*? How do you propose all of us can *voyager en vacances*?'

In the Rolls, Mariette said, mistakenly thinking her father had now been fully won over. She threw her arms around his neck and kissed him. Pop knew he was finished. 'Perfick, and toot sweet I suppose?' He sighed wearily. Arrangements were left to Ma and Mariette who very efficiently organised an air ferry flight for the family, the Rolls and Oscar's pram.

Travelling with a number of somewhat more sophisticated

passengers, the family arrived in France only a few days later. Once the fearful horror of crossing the Channel and getting the hang of driving on the wrong side of the road was overcome, Pop's good humour returned. The weather wasn't that good, but at least it wasn't pouring. The children had been singing, in their best French, in the back and now, after four hours on the road, Ma decided that lunch was long overdue. Charley soon spotted a café and Pop pulled up. He needed some convincing, as all the lorries outside made him suspect that this was some low-class transport caff. Charley explained that you could rely on good food in a routier. Besides, Montgomery was desperate for a piddle.

The Larkin family were seated at a long table and with the arrival of pâté, then lamb chops, steak frites, vegetables and masses of wonderful bread, Pop started to gain a little confidence in the dreaded foreign food. Charley had been on the phone to confirm their booking at the hotel. Management had changed since he was last there, he reported, but all seemed to be in order. He poured red wine from the jug on the table and set about his biff teck.

There was still a fair way to go, so they didn't linger over lunch. It was late afternoon by the time they approached St-Pierre-le-Port, driving, it seemed, against a great wave of traffic heading away from the coast. Pop was worried. Did that lot know something he didn't? Charley explained that as it was the end of August the French would have finished their vacances and were driving home to Paris or wherever. Even Pop was shocked at some of the instances of bad driving and bad manners they encountered on the road, but the Rolls acted like some iron-clad diplomatic immunity and wherever there was a fracas or contretemps the Larkin family were waved regally through.

The weather had not been improving. By the time they reached the little port, there was a gale blowing and the fishing boats at their moorings were tossing about violently. Canvas awnings were flapping loudly in front of cafés and beach chairs were flung into the air by the wind. Spirits drooped.

'Where have we come to, Charley? Lapland?'

'Not a soul out of doors,' said Ma.

'Temporary squall, I expect,' answered Charley lamely. 'The hotel's just over there.' He pointed along the front. Charley nearly died when they pulled up. There was barely a hint of the trim, brightly painted façade he remembered. The delapidation made Home Farm look like the Ritz. Blistered paintwork, sagging balconies, dim lighting from within and a pile of broken cane furniture on the front terrace ... He cleared his throat. 'Looks much better in sunlight. Don't worry.'

Arrival at the Hôtel Beau Rivage was inauspicious. It did not seem like the start of the holiday of a lifetime.

It was also so much smaller than Charley remembered, but that is always the way of childhood memories, *n'est-ce pas?*

Charley took charge of things in the dingy foyer where their arrival was greeted with hostility by Eugène Mollet, the desk clerk. He told Pop, struggling with the baggage, that there was no porter. Mariette wrinkled her nose against the smell of French cigarettes. Ma thought the pong was actually leaking gas or mice. Mollet dealt with the reservations and passports with disdain. Their rooms weren't even ready but at least they were offered tea in the lounge. Tea turned out to be a pot of hot water, some tea bags on strings and a plate of lemon slices. Ma almost wept. So did Pa when he saw the bill. Then he discovered there was no television in the hotel. He surveyed the threadbare room, saw the rain gushing down the window panes and asked Ma what the merry Ellen were they doing there. There was a particularly nasty moment when Ma, stuck in a wicker chair and unable to dislodge it from her massive bottom was pompously informed by Mollet that it was a serious matter to damage hotel furniture.

This was the last straw for Pop. 'Now you just *écoutez moi, mon ami. Qu'est-ce qu'il y a?* And *comment ça va* and *comment allez-vous bien dormi* and *qu'est-ce que vous avez mangé* and *à bientôt, sans faire* and all that caper. *Comprenez-vous?* We want a bit more of the jolly old entente cordiale, *mon brave*, and you get those room keys toot sweet, otherwise *vous êtes in très* deep trouble *avec moi*, savvy?' It was one of the longest speeches Pop had made in his life. The fact that some, at least, of it was in French of a sort was little short of miraculous. Mollet removed his pince-nez in astonishment and hurried away.

'That was perfick, Pop,' said Ma. '*Très* perfickly *bon*.' At last the rooms were declared ready. They were all awful. The twins were in an attic room that barely had space for their bunks. Montgomery was squeezed into a little triangular partition. Primrose and Victoria appeared to have to share the bottom drawer of the wardrobe in their room and the doubles for Ma and Pop and Charley and Mariette weren't much better: threadbare, grubby, rickety furniture, nonexistent plumbing and chilly. Everyone wanted to go straight home, though no one admitted it out loud.

Ma tried to console Pop with remarks about their forthcoming slap-up dinner, but he wanted a drink to be going on with. The hotel, he was informed, did not provide room service. Pop's face was as thunderous as the weather outside. Oscar began to bawl.

Finally Oscar was pacified and Pop and Ma went downstairs to join the others in the dining room. Six

Primrose

Primrose was only twelve but Pop could see that, given a few years, she might become even more beautiful than Mariette. She had the same olive skin and great dark eyes, although while Mariette's eyes flashed, Primrose's smouldered.

She was an early starter where an interest in the opposite sex was concerned. First of all it was Charley, whom she adored with an anguished envy - when she grew up she wanted to find someone just like him and meanwhile she was burningly jealous of Mariette. When the family went to France she was quick to make friends with Marc-Antoine, a serious boy who looked just like Marlon Brando when he took his glasses off. She persuaded Ma to persuade Pop to allow her to go back to Paris and spend a few weeks with Marc-Antoine and his family. All four parents agreed that it would help both youngsters with their languages. But it was when she was a little older that Primrose - or rather the curate - met her Waterloo. From the moment she met him, Primrose knew that Mr Candy was the man for her.

Brainy, bookish, fond of quoting Keats and John Donne, Primrose was probably the brainbox of the family. How unfair that anyone should be so doubly blessed and how extraordinary that despite these handicaps she retained a sweet nature and a lot of common sense.

chattering French families were silenced by Ma's entrance: she'd dressed for the occasion in gauzy mauve silk with silver ornaments in her hair and great diamanté danglers in her ears. Pop stepped behind her, proud of her regal sway. They must have munched through six baguettes between them before the waitress brought them menus.Well, at least they could have langoustines and Breton sausage and frites ... things were looking up. Pop fancied the pigeon. The waitress shook her head. Mostly the things on the menu were off. She could offer them fried sardines and then rabbit. Or cold sliced mutton. With boiled potatoes. They dined grimly and quietly.

Next day the weather was a little better and the family decided they must make the best of things. Like a military operation they trooped to the beach with all the paraphernalia of a sun-bathing army: buckets and spades, lilos, beach-balls, snorkels, flippers, parasols, draught screens. Ma had put her favourite swimming costume on beneath her beach wrap and Mariette had inched herself into the tiniest two-piece Kent could provide. Pop surveyed the silver sand for a good spot for the family to pitch camp. The locals had already taken most of the nicer spots near the water's edge but Pop negotiated some space for himself and his clan, breathed in the sharp Atlantic air and pronounced it perfick. Mariette remarked that the water was freezing.

Ma took off her wrap and Pa gazed up and down her creamy, rounded enormity. 'Perfick,' he repeated. She was attracting some attention from French groups on the beach. Pa put it down to the fact that all French women were undernourished, like Brigitte Bardot, and they'd forgotten what a really womanly woman was. The twins and Victoria splashed happily in the sea, Primrose painted her toenails, Ma and Mariette, oiled like oven-basted roasting birds, stretched out and basked in the warmth. Oscar slept happily beneath his parasol. Charley read while Pop, a mug of cider and a cigar to hand, felt contented at last. Montgomery was looking for shrimps. Pop fondly rubbed more oil into Ma's back when she turned over. Oh yes, things were looking up.

Mariette caused something of a stir when she rose to buy some chestnuts from a vendor who was working the beach. In her tiny scarlet bikini and with her perfect curvy figure she knowingly distracted a group of young Frenchmen who were persuing some strange and apparently pointless ball-game nearby. They were certainly well built, those young fellers, thought Ma, as she watched them resume their beach exercises, calling out to each other. 'Alphonse', 'Xavier', 'Claude', 'Jean-Pierre'...

'Why do they have to have such stupid names?' Pop wondered.

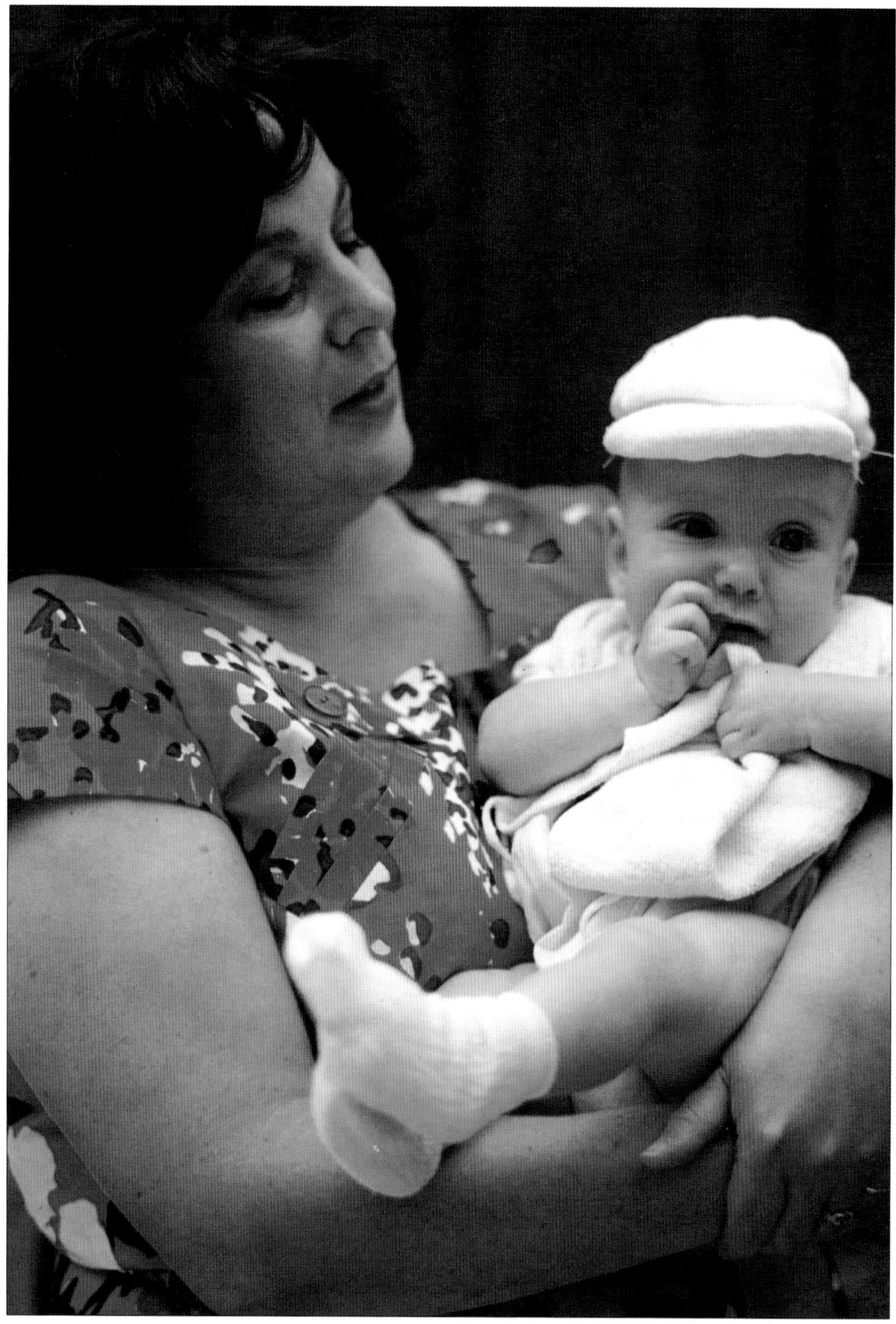

Ma with Oscar, a late addition to the Larkin family.

Primrose mooched up to sit between him and Ma. She thought that one of the French boys had been staring at her. 'Which one?' asked Ma. Primrose indicated a lean boy with glasses, probably about twelve. Ma was reassured. He reminded her of Charley. 'Seems a nice boy, Primrose.'

Primrose was not mollified. The boy, she claimed, was forever looking at her through his telescope. Pop couldn't really blame the little blighter. Primrose was well set to be as great a beauty as Mariette and didn't seem to be aware of the fact as yet, thank God. Ma started talking about going to one of the villages, twenty miles along the coast, where there was some kind of fête taking place the next day. Mariette wasn't keen, she wanted to work on her tan and Pop wanted to get the thermostat on the Rolls fixed. Charley, however, was game. He wondered if they could go there on the little train he remembered from his childhood. He was a little hurt that Mariette seemed so indifferent, and returned to his book, barely aware that Mariette was constantly having to throw back the ball to the French boys. They seemed to deliberately mis-hit so that she had to throw it back to them.

Finally he noticed and said something. 'Are those louts annoying you?'

'No. They're just having fun.'

'Sounds as if you'd like to join in.'

'Course not. I'm just watching.'

Mariette didn't object to watching young men as well formed as those boys, as Primrose darkly observed.

By the end of the day Primrose had done some entente cordiale herself and had changed her mind about the French boy with glasses, Marc-Antoine. She thought he might be rather nice, as Ma had observed, and made a date to see him on the beach the following day.

Back in the hotel Pop had to overcome yet another obstacle. Lord, he thought, it had seemed as if everything had got itself sorted out but now there was this problem with the passports. Mollet, or Molly as Pop thought of him by now, pointed out that all the kids were registered on Pop's passport but that Ma, Florence Daisy Parker, was a single woman. It was thus highly irregular that she and Pop should be sharing a room.

'I regret I must ask you to leave the hotel,' said Mollet coldly.

'Listen Eugène, old son. Not on your nelly.'

'Nelly?'

'Rhubarb. Don't bother.'

Mollet graciously explained that if the family left quietly there would be no charge for their one night stay, not even for the chair Madame destroyed last night. Pop was having none of this and demanded to see the boss, Mademoiselle Dupont. Mollet flinched and excused himself. Pop straightened his hair in the lobby's mirror and waited for Antoinette Dupont to arrive.

Ma and the children went to the procession at Ville de Fougères, along the coast.

She was a tall, slender woman somewhere in her thirties, severe in a black dress and with straight dark hair pulled away from her face. Despite the trace of a moustache and that dull olive skin that so many French women have, Pop thought she was quite attractive in a way.

'I hear you're throwing us out,' he stated.

Mademoiselle Dupont clutched at her bunch of keys and explained that there were certain niceties that had to be observed. Pop agreed with her. Their bed for instance, was rather uncomfortable, and the rooms were all very cramped. And couldn't she do something about the window in Mariette and Charley's room. It wouldn't open and they'd had no air all night. And, Pop went on, he thought it shouldn't be too much trouble for the restaurant to provide soft-boiled eggs at breakfast. Antoinette Dupont was wilting under this attack.

'M'sieu Larkin,' she began faintly. 'We still havn't resolved the matter of a double room being occupied by single persons ...'

'If me and Ma don't mind, why should you?' She explained that there was a problem with the police. Such arrangements were against the law in France. Pop was amazed. He'd thought that it was all ooh la la and *à bientôt* in France. Couldn't Mamselle break the rules for once? She looked down to Pop. He was smiling in his most winning way, and then winked.

'I'll see,' she sighed.

'Perfick,' said Pop.

Next morning, all that silly nonsense sorted out, Pop waved off Ma and Oscar, the twins, Victoria, Montgomery, Mariette and Charley onto the bus that would take them to the festival in a nearby town. Then he took the Rolls to the local garage where they found it an honour to tinker with such a noble

The family was fascinated by the display of Breton customs.

engine. He chatted for a while with Maurice the mechanic who spoke a little English. Maurice had clearly assumed that Pop was some kind of aristo, and kept addressing him as milord. It was all to do with the monograms on the Rolls, Pop knew. 'So much more impressive than on handkerchiefs and shirts, wouldn't you agree, m'lord? Especially vulgar on shirts.'

'Yes, well, how much do I owe you?' asked Pop. 'No charge, m'lord. It's an honour.'

The others had a lovely day in the little cobbled town where the festival was held. Charley enjoyed showing off his French and knowledge of local history, the girls loved seeing the young women in their Breton costumes and high lace hats and all of them ate enough creamy pastries to make many other people horribly sick. All in all, a very successful outing.

Primrose enjoyed her day too. Marc-Antoine was a serious boy away from his friends and they spent hours describing their homes and backgrounds. Paris, thought Primrose, sounded so much more exciting than Home Farm. Marc-Antoine explained that his father was a pâtissier and Primrose said that Pop was a farmer, in a sweeping, general way.

She told Pop about it on the beach. He was enjoying having a day to himself, calling for drinks from the waiters who worked the beach, and he

Pop was enjoying a quiet day to himself for a change.

was touched that Primrose, who'd become a bit introverted lately, confided in him. Marc-Antoine had invited her to lunch the next day, to meet his family, she said. Pop thought this sounded rather fine. Entente cordiale if ever he'd come across it. In the hotel Maurice the mechanic was having lunch with the gloomy Mollet and referring to his morning's work on the m'lord's Roller. Mademoiselle Dupont entered the room and overheard the last part of the conversation.

'You mean he's an English lordship?'

'You don't have monogrammed doors on a Rolls for nothing. When I addressed him by his title he did not demur.' Maurice continued with his lunch. Antoinette Dupont moved to the window and pondered the eccentricities of the English aristocrats. They dressed like peasants, spoke like peasants and ate like peasants. They bred like rabbits, had shabby luggage and drank like fishes. Yes, she supposed, it was obvious really. M'sieu Larkin was a true milord and she would thank Mollet to remember it.

Ma's trip to the little town along the

coast had been crowned by an encounter with Gérard Brisson, her friend from Ramsgate. She couldn't wait to tell Pop about it. Brisson had been thrilled to see her again, flirted in a way that Ma found très charming and invited her and Oscar aboard his boat again. They had a very jolly trip round the bay and Gérard even offered to sail them back to St-Pierre-le-Port. Ma declined but she did cook lunch on board for Gérard and his crew. Even that tiny galley, where Ma's girth could have been a problem, did not prevent her from cooking the nicest lunch those matelots had enjoyed for a very long time. Over a few glasses with Gérard Brisson Ma was able, quite unwittingly, to lay the foundation stones of another bit of entente cordiale that Pop would soon have good reason to be very cheerful about.

Ma reluctantly disembarked, kissed by every member of the crew. To her surprise she was greeted by Angela Snow on the quay. Angela explained that she and her sister Iris were staying nearby. Wasn't this coincidence a scream? In fact they were there because Iris was keen to visit all the religious sights in Brittany, particularly now, when all the little towns were having their festivals. Angela raised her brows and pulled a face at Ma. It was perfectly clear that Angela wasn't all that keen on the holy-joe but Ma thought it was nice that she was keeping her sister company. They were staying quite near St-Pierre-le-Port, actually, and Angela offered Ma and Oscar a lift home, but she explained she had to meet the others to take the bus. They made a promise to meet up.

Pop had come to an arrangement with Antoinette Dupont. Now that she realised that he was an English milord, nothing was too good for him and she would give up her own room for him and Ma. Quite the nicest room in the hotel, with a lovely view over the harbour – Pop was well pleased. He wondered for a moment about displaying his gratitude in a practical way ... Antoinette had changed her thick lisle stockings for sheer black silk ones and Pop had enjoyed following her upstairs ... the silky legs, the well-tailored black skirt sleek around her bottom. But no, Ma was due back any moment now. Yes, he said to Antoinette, this new room was quite perfick. There was even a little annexe, just right for Oscar's cot.

'Very kind of you, Mademoiselle Dupont. Very kind indeed. The room is perfick, right down to the smell of lily-of-the-valley.'

She was surprised. But these English milords with their famous love of the countryside ... of course he would know it was her scent. 'May I say it's a pleasure to deal with a real Englishman, compared to some of these new tourists. You are so restrained, so much in control, a man of the world.'

Gérard Brisson took Ma for a trip around the bay. She cooked lunch in return.

'And you're a real sweetheart.' Pop gave her a kiss on the cheek and a pat on the rear. Antoinette Dupont almost fainted. She didn't give a hoot if a couple of her other guests glimpsed her standing there with that beatific smile. They could think what they liked and rot in hell for all she cared. The English milord, Milord Larkin, was her main priority from now on.

All together and getting into the swing of life on the continent.

EPISODE 6

A Breath of French Air

PART TWO

By now, the Larkin family had the French taped. Pop had come to an understanding with Mademoiselle Dupont and soft-boiled eggs for breakfast were no longer a problem. Primrose was getting on so famously with young Marc-Antoine that there was already talk of her staying with his family in Paris for a month. The twins and Monty grew browner by the day on the beach. Even Molly, as Pop now called the stiffly pince-nezed clerk at the desk, was showing respect to Milord Larkin of Sidcup. Only Charley and Mariette seemed just a *petit peu* subdued. Pop was dismayed to see Charley cross the terrace on his way to the beach with two books under his arm. What on earth did a young chap need books for in a place like this? With Mariette, for heaven's sake?

He was watching his son-in-law's back when Ma remembered that they'd run into Angela. She explained that Angela was staying in another hotel with her nun-like sister - very keen on shrines, Ma noted mysteriously. Pop, of course, was delighted to hear that his favourite popsy was in the area.

On the beach, Charley was in a quiet fury. He thought that Mariette, sensational today in a cinnamon-coloured boned swimsuit, was flirting shamelessly with the athletic French boys. She denied it, but she didn't seem keen on his offer of a book or his suggestion that they take the little train for an excursion. She wanted to work on her tan, she said, without opening her eyes. Nothing to stop Charley going on his precious train alone, was there? Hurt and angry Charley picked up his timetable and walked to the station by himself.

'Enjoy your choo choo, Charley,' she murmured to herself as he departed. 'Off in a huff to your chuff chuff chuff ...'

Things weren't going Charley's way. He was informed at the station that the train he wanted was cancelled - there would be a wait of at least an hour and the stationmaster recommended the bar next door. Sitting morosely with a newspaper, Charley was bullied into conversation by a striking, mannish redhead. 'I'm Max to my friends. Maxine to idiots.' She called impatiently for service and at last Gabby, the stationmaster, appeared. It was his bar. She order a 'Mendiant au Cheval' - pernod, egg yolk, rum and a dash of cognac. Charley remarked that it sounded like his father-in-law's kind of drink. At her insistence he tried one. And another, and another ...

Max, it seemed, was a successful painter. She was regaling the bar with some rather risqué anecdote regarding a nude model and the Mayor when Gérard Brisson walked in. Fuzzily Charley realised that this must be Ma's handsome skipper and introduced himself. He still rather hoped to take that train-ride, but squint as he might, he couldn't make much sense of the

Pop borrowed a suit for the ceremony to honour Monsieur Mollet's brother-in-law.

board next door at the station. Gabby, now in his cap and jacket again, steered him by the elbow back to the bar and suggested he have another drink. The train, he said, was delayed. It was lunchtime.

Across the bay, Primrose and Marc-Antoine walked through the iron gates of a large, opulent villa. 'It's beautiful. I thought you were staying in a hotel like us.'

Marc-Antoine shrugged. 'We always come here in the summer.' His father, it transpired, was no humble pâtissier but the owner of a giant national chain of shops. Primrose was impressed but his parents welcomed her in that French way which is both warm and casual. She felt quite comfortable. Marc-Antoine, whose manner bordered on the pompous at all times and whose glasses lent him an owlish air, produced his telescope, usually tucked like a swagger stick under his arm. He trained the glass at the station and focused on the happily swaying figure of Charley - still waiting for his little train.

After lunch the pair found Pop playing ping pong with the twins and Victoria. Pop looked alarmed when they passed on the news of Charley-spotting. He tore over to the bar where Charley was, by now, once again

Some of the French food was delicious, but not quite the same as Ma's home cooking.

ensconced and out for the count, while Max was singing some Parisian boulevard number. Gabby gave Pop a drink and effected introductions all round. Pop shook hands with Brisson and sipped his drink. His eyes widened after the first taste. 'That's very nearly perfick.'

Gérard Brisson clapped Pop's shoulder. 'You are a tough customer, as your charming wife told me. She came for a trip on my boat yesterday, with little Oscar. Your wife is a splendid cook, M'sieu. Did she tell you how she prepared a meal for us all?'

Later, Pop took another gulp of the cocktail that had been Charley's ruin. This was an opportunity if ever he'd seen one. 'That's something I want to talk to you about Admiral. Your eating habits.'

Pop took Charley back to the hotel in the Rolls, countering the disapproving glances they recieved from the elderly spinsters as they passed through the hotel lobby with a remark about how nasty sunstroke could be. 'Here we go Charley. Nice little kip and you'll be right as rain. Ready for afternoon tea.' Mademoiselle Dupont, skittishly patting her new hairdo, asked if she could help but Pop said he'd manage. On his way out Molly grabbed him ominously and said that he'd like a word in private. Pop thought it might be more bother over the passports and followed Mollet apprehensively into the lounge. What a day, and it was only just past lunchtime.

But Mollet, it seemed, was seeking a favour. Addressing Pop throughout as M'lord he explained that his eldest sister, the seventy-year-old widow of a Resistance hero, was very ill and that it would cheer her last days if an English milord could come and pay his respects. Her husband's bravery had never been acknowledged by the French. Pop was both scandalised and touched that Molly should ask him to do the honours. This, he felt, was a kind of justification for allowing the milord business to go uncorrected. After all, he only had to present some sort of scroll. Molly was making a note of details. 'You are, let me see, Lord Larkin of Seedcup?'

Pop was distracted by something outside. 'Sidcup, yes, Seedcup.' He looked out towards the beach again. There was a good bit of détente going on there, in a manner of speaking.

Charley had pulled round in his room with a good deal of cold water and deep breaths of fresh air. From the window that he had torn open, he was horrified to see Mariette playing beach-ball with the bronzed young Frenchmen on the beach. Steady on his feet now, but still far from sober, he strode across the beach, past a startled Ma, and set about puncturing every French beach-ball in sight with a knife. Then he gave Sebastien, the most handsome of the French boys and the one Mariette seemed to like best, a powerful kick in the derrière and dragged Mariette up from her reclining position.

'Tomorrow you can forget about the beach and these fol de rols. You're coming on the train with me!' Mariette was silent. Pop ran across from the hotel to ask Ma what all the fuss had been over and she looked fondly and wisely at Charley and Mariette. Just a little tiff, a bit of local difficulty, and all sorted out now, she was sure.

'Next week's their wedding anniversary. They'll be springing a tiny surprise on us soon, I shouldn't wonder.' Ma was quietly confident as ever.

Next day Pop, in a borrowed dark suit, a range of medals provided by Molly and with a paper Union Jack attached to the bonnet of the Rolls, arrived at the cemetery with Molly in the passenger seat. A small knot of locals were gathered around a grave, the older men wearing medals and old service caps, the women all in black and looking gloomy. The ancient Hortense leaned on a stick and smiled weakly as Molly arrived with the milord. Pop was introduced with great aplomb and proceeded to behave as Lord Larkin of Seedcup should. On

Monsieur Mollet was a tough nut to crack but he couldn't resist the Larkin charm.

Milord Larkin of Seedcup delivers his tribute to a neglected hero of the Resistance.

behalf of the grateful British people, let alone Her Majesty's Government, he presented le Scroll d'Honneur to Madame Fontanet, Hortense. He made his speech with fitting dignity:
'... without fear and consideration for his own safety to assist personnel of the Royal Air Force to escape to freedom and continue to fight for the liberation of France. This scroll is in his revered memory and thus presented this day by me,' Pop baulked at actually verbalising his recent elevation to the peerage, 'Sydney Charles Larkin, yours truly etc.' The bugle sounded. Pop presented the scroll to the tearful widow and went, with relief, to the Rolls by himself.

Angela Snow happened to be on a bus passing the cemetery as Pop pulled out. She hammered on the window, and made the driver stop so that she could clamber out and hurry over to the Rolls. Pop was delighted to see her. As they drove along the coast road Angela complained that Iris was not an ideal holiday companion. Too keen on prayers and quoting from ecclesiastical guidebooks. Meeting Pop like this was a real bonus. She stretched and asked Pop if he felt like some lunch. 'Perfick,' said Pop. 'Jolly good idea. Where shall we go?'

Angela knew a place along the coast where the food was pretty awful but the atmosphere wonderful. You could eat al fresco by the dunes at the edge of the forest. Pop changed into a sports shirt and a pair of shorts, slung the day before into the back of the Rolls and followed Angela's directions to a primitive restaurant - little more than a shack and a barbeque - a short way along the coast. Pierre told them what was on today. Mussels, steak, some brie and some wine. Oh yes, some rosy, rosy wine ...

Angela was deliciously mischievous as they attacked their steaks. What did he think of Mademoiselle Dupont and had Pop gone in for any fraternity? After lunch, they dozed, they swam, they kissed a little bit and dozed again. Pop lay with his arms around Angela Snow and gazed up into the perfect blue sky. Her skin was warm and brown against his. This was just too perfick for words. In the late afternoon a breeze ruffled the sand at their feet and Pop knew it was time to drive home. He kissed Angela's sleek blonde head and said they'd better make tracks. She smiled her slow, open smile and took Pop's hand on the short walk to the car.

It had been such an exhausting day that Ma felt she just had to have a bottle of Bolly before going to sleep. Pop was despatched to fetch it, and took the opportunity of a quick little flirt with Antoinette Dupont. She was ever more impressed by Pop - the milord was drinking Bollinger as a nightcap. What a man! Pop carried the bottle and glasses upstairs and was ambushed at the top of the stairs by Primrose who insisted on talking to him in the bathroom. It was important and private and she didn't want to wake Victoria. By now Pop was prepared for anything and he was almost relieved to learn that it was only about Primrose spending some time in Paris with Marc-Antoine's family. Ma had said 'Ask Pop', which meant yes. So Pop was really a bit of a pushover ... By the time he got back to their room Ma was fast asleep. Pop set the tray down and decided to leave the Bolly for another day.

Angela and Iris came over for tea the next day. The plan was to take advantage of Mariette and Charley's absence on the train to plot their anniversary dinner. They roped in Mademoiselle Dupont. With all the children, Marc-Antoine's parents, Mademoiselle Dupont, the Snow sisters it was going to be a round dozen. The hotel, at the end of the season, would be quiet, so the Larkin party could commandeer the dining room. They settled on a menu of melon with port, roast beef and all the trimmings (Iris volunteered to cook the Yorkshire), jelly and custard for the children and crêpes Suzettes. Alphonse, the chef, was very excited - mainly, if unaccountably, by Iris. Angela raised an elegant eyebrow towards Pop. Maybe if she taught him about Yorkshire he'd reciprocate with stuffing ... Perhaps Alphonse would show her a little shrine he knew ... At any rate, he was making heroic headway with the cognac as they discussed the meal and Pop, in the best of humours once more, beamed fondly at them all and

Angela Snow

Angela Snow was a glorious, tawny blonde, who stood four inches taller than Pop - there was little she liked better than looking down into his eyes. The two adored each other. Angela was the daughter of a distinguished Queen's Council, Sir John Furlington-Snow, but she never used her full name. She didn't seem to work but she was always busy. She was, as Pop would put it, 'rolling in it', but unlike many wealthy people she was generosity itself. Pop had a feeling that when she was in London she had a very wild time indeed, but down in Kent she had eyes only for him. Ma smiled benignly at this harmless flirtation. She was happy to 'lend Pop out' from time to time. The variety was good for him.

Pop and Angela had met at the great party the Larkins held after the gymkhana. It was the first of many smooches. He was charmed by her combination of tomboy athleticism and dazzling, golden-haired glamour. She was enchanted by his wit and raffish energy. She became a regular visitor to Home Farm and was not averse to flirting shamelessly with the Brigadier when he was there too.

When the Larkins went to Brittany Angela, by coincidence, was staying just along the coast with her dowdy sister Iris. Angela and Pop had a wickedly indulgent lunch together one day, followed by a long, intoxicating cuddle on the dunes afterwards. Just the sort of thing Iris needed, thought Angela, and managed to get her fixed up with a French chef ...

A superb horsewoman, a great tennis player, a skilled, if slightly reckless driver, a terrific dancer and heroic drinker, Angela really was Pop's kind of woman. One of these days, he thought, one of these days ...

pronounced all the arrangements 'perfick'.

At sunset, shielded by a beach screen, Pop and Ma lay on the beach drinking last night's untouched Bollinger. They agreed Primrose could stay on in France. For her education, Ma said. Not half, Pop nodded. Ma had a brief worry that Marc-Antoine's parents might be intimidated by the Rolls and said Pop ought to park it round the back of the hotel for the evening of the party.

Iris was definitely getting into the swing of things, helping Alphonse to choose the freshest, crispest vegetables and enjoying his intelligent conversation. He'd suggested that they went walking and meditating together some time and she thought this a splendid idea. Pop had bought one of Max's paintings as a present for Charley and Mariette - and impulsively asked her to the party - and Ma had made Pop buy her a shimmering silvery bedspread that passed for a dress from one of the boutiques. Charley and Mariette spent a blissful day together, quite oblivious to all the preparations.

The dining room was being decorated with flags and bunting by Molly. Bowls of flowers were everywhere, tables had been pushed together to form one long seating area. Alphonse was sweating in the kitchen. Charley and Mariette were taking tea in their room, having been refused access to the dining room which puzzled them only briefly. Pop was mixing a lethal punch in the kitchen with Mademoiselle Dupont. Everyone spoke in whispers and the hotel was oddly quiet. Charley remarked upon this and Mariette said it must be something to do with the end of the season. She set her tea cup down and stretched her arms round Charley's neck. 'Our last night. Haven't we had a lovely holiday?'

'Perfect. Perfick,' said Charley.

In the kitchen Antoinette Dupont shyly presented Pop with a pair of silver cuff-links bearing his very own monogram. '*Un petit cadeau*,' she blushed.

'Very perfick. Chick. Er, *très snob*', said Pop, so touched that he just couldn't help sweeping her into his arms for a long, light kiss.

Everyone was getting ready for dinner. Best dresses, flashiest jewellery, dusty old tuxes. The Gammelins, Marc-Antoine's parents, had arrived early and parked their Rolls behind the hotel so as not to seem ostentatious. Molly showed them into the dining room. Mademoiselle Dupont, elegant in black silk, checked on Alphonse in the kitchen where Iris was fussing over her Yorkshire. Quietly all the other guests slipped into the dining room, the younger girls very grown up with touches of make-up, Monty in a matelot sweater, Angela ravishing in swathed turquoise silk ... Charley and

Mariette stepped downstairs and were deflected from the usual bar by Molly. Drinks tonight, he said, were in the dining room.

They were astonished. The room so gaily decorated, their family and friends waiting with glasses raised, Pop's picture by Max on an easel in the corner with a loving message, a huge cake ... Pop hushed the clapping and made his speech, thanking everyone and sending his love, most of all, to Mariette and Charley.

The meal was a triumph, especially the rosbif. Alphonse was congratulated and toasted as was Iris for her Yorkshire. The sophisticated Gammelins thought that the custard and jelly were *formidable* and M'sieu G was already wondering how he could market it in his national chain of shops. Pop saw his contemplative expression and whispered to Angela, 'Shopkeepers. Live hand to mouth I expect.'

Then there was dancing. Iris rather wanted to dance with Alphonse and sought him out in the kitchen. He professed a desire to meditate a little on the sand dunes and Iris thought this might be just the ticket. She works in the kitchen of the Hôtel Beau Rivage to this day.

The singing and dancing and seconds of pudding went on for hours. Eventually everyone was exhausted.

Antoinette Dupont was sad to see Milord Larkin and his family drive away. It was the end of the summer, the end of the season. She hoped she would see them all again. She glanced at Molly. He was blowing his nose.

Only a kilometre away Ma called out, 'Slow down. It's Primrose!' She was sitting on a bank eating an ice cream with Marc-Antoine.

'Doesn't give a monkey's, does she?' asked Pop, waving his cigar.

'It's the French air, innit?' Ma replied.

''Spect it is. Perfick.'

TEA TENT

Postscript

A national nerve was struck by *The Darling Buds of May*. No one could have predicted that it would capture the public's imagination to the extent that it did, that Pop would become as great a national hero as Gazza. David Jason, already hugely popular from other television roles such as *Only Fools and Horses*, played Pop so faithfully to H.E. Bates's creation that it is now difficult to imagine any other actor in the role. Ma, Mariette and every other member of the family were also perfectly cast, as were secondary characters.

Why was it that *The Darling Buds of May* won the hearts of viewers all over Britain? When have the tabloid newspapers and the usually solemn Sunday broadsheets been equally enchanted by a television series? There is no simple answer. Well-crafted scripts and consummate acting were important, of course, but other factors, layer upon layer, contributed to its appeal to young and old, wealthy and unemployed, cultured and unsophisticated.

It was Pop Larkin's world that everyone envied. A countryside that was unbesmirched by motorways and factories. A world where the thoroughly worthy but sometimes tiresome rules of the late twentieth century had not even been thought of. No seat-belt regulations or parking meters, no real public fear about drinking or eating too much. No pin-thin ideal of womanhood ... Pop managed to have it all - a wife he adored, but harmless diversions with other women, a marvellous family life without the chains of marriage, a good time and a roll of notes in his pocket but no drudgery in an office, the knack of making the most loyal of friends and besting his few enemies ... and he paid no income tax.

In Pop's country the sun always shone and the harvest never failed. People returned good turns, children grew up with strong brown limbs and social delinquency was something that you might learn about from a flickering black and white television. There was money to be made if you knew the right man and you spent it on life's pleasures - food, drink, holidays, outings, nice things to wear, parties and big cigars. Above all there was the timeless, restorative beauty of the natural world that surrounded him.

It is easy to understand why all this struck a chord in the Britain of the late 1950s where rationing was still a very recent memory and where so many families were still recovering from the privations and personal losses of the war. Pop's life exemplified a peace and a plenty that had always been something of a fantasy but which people were nonetheless nostalgic for. In Pop's world a little black-marketeering was legitimate barter, not shameless racketeering, and he was the person everyone wanted to be: the one who got away with it, the winner.

The appeal in the 1990s is less obvious, but really much the same. In a time of recession and cut-backs it was glorious to see a man like Pop Larkin getting things his own way, beating the system and not with bombs or demonstrations or ludicrous hours in the City, but with charm and native cunning. With more and more people disillusioned with city life and the pressures of holding rather dismal lives together, Pop's lifestyle was a perfect dream. The television, on Sunday evenings, was something that shored up millions of viewers, dreading Monday morning, and sent them away comforted, happier and, perhaps, more concerned than before about the preservation of the good things in their own lives.

Pop will be back next year in a new series. His yard will not be much changed but the children will have grown up a little. Tiny hints of 'progress' will have subtly entered his world. A new cocktail called Moon Rocket, dark rumours about something called the Common Market and even talk of a tunnel across the channel. Pop will be ready to meet every challenge and in essence his world will not have changed. Edith, the Brigadier, Angela and Mademoiselle Dupont will still figure in his life and that of the family. The wish-fulfilment will continue and Pop's Kentish paradise is eternal.

The genius of H.E. Bates has been rightly rediscovered in Yorkshire Television's superb series. His understanding of Pop's kind of country life, as opposed to the Jerebohms', has been hilariously shown. The quiet good humour of the books, their celebration of all that is natural - in the woods and fields and between human beings in all the many kinds of relationships they might have - have been rediscovered. The television series was a triumphant celebration of Pop Larkin's world and it doesn't really matter if that world never really existed. H.E. Bates understood our need to believe that it existed, and our desire to embrace it.

Credits

THE DARLING BUDS OF MAY EPISODE ONE

Adapted by Bob Larbey
Producer Robert Banks Stewart
Director Rodney Bennett

Pop Larkin
DAVID JASON
Ma Larkin
PAM FERRIS
Charley
PHILIP FRANKS
Mariette
CATHERINE ZETA JONES
Brigadier
MORAY WATSON
Edith Pilchester
RACHEL BELL
Salesman
RAYMOND MASON
Jack Woodley
ROWLAND DAVIES
Mrs Peele
TRICIA THORNS
George Carter
PAUL WILLIAMSON
Freda O' Connor
WENDY WILLIAMS
Miss Borden
JOY SHELTON
Montgomery
IAN TUCKER
Primrose
JULIE DAVIS
Petunia
CHRISTINA GILES
Zinnia
KATHERINE GILES
Victoria
STEPHANIE RALPH

Production Manager
DAVID NOBLE
1st Assistant Director
IAN MORLEY
Location Manager
MENZIES KENNEDY
Stage Manager
ANTON DARBY
Production Assistant
LIZ WADDELL
Unit Assistant
STUART BARLOW
Production Secretary
KAREN BARKER
Production Buyer
BOB BAYNE
Chargehand Props
DAVE PROCTER
Chargehand Electrician
MAL IRWIN
Camera Operator
DAVE CAREY
Sound Recordist
LEE CORBETT
Dubbing Mixer
STEVE HAYNES
Dubbing Editor
ALAN WILLIS
Titles
PAUL PEPPIATE
Casting
MALCOLM DRURY
Costume Designer
BRIAN CASTLE
Make Up Designer
PAM FOX
Title Theme
PIP BURLEY
Music
BARRIE GUARD
Editor
IAN MALLETT
Designer
ALAN DAVIS
Director of Photography
PETER JACKSON BSC
Produced in association with
EXCELSIOR GROUP PRODUCTIONS
Executive Producers
VERNON LAWRENCE
RICHARD BATES

THE DARLING BUDS OF MAY EPISODE TWO

Adapted by Bob Larbey
Producer Robert Banks Stewart
Director Rodney Bennett

Pop Larkin
DAVID JASON
Ma Larkin
PAM FERRIS
Charley
PHILIP FRANKS
Mariette
CATHERINE ZETA JONES
Brigadier
MORAY WATSON
Edith Pilchester
RACHEL BELL
Sir George Bluff-Gore
MICHAEL CULVER
Lady Bluff-Gore
RICHENDA CAREY
Angela Snow
KIKA MIRYLEES
Mr Shell
PETER GALE
Mrs Hall
SHIRLEY CAIN
Pauline Jackson
ANNA SKYE
Poll
ARBEL JONES
Lil
JANE WOOD
Mr Jennings
DAVID SQUIRE
Aunt Fran
JILL RICHARDS
Jack Woodley
ROWLAND DAVIES
Freda O'Connor
WENDY WILLIAMS
Edna Barnwell
ANNIE LOON
Effie Barnwell
HILARY SESTA
Montgomery
IAN TUCKER
Primrose
JULIE DAVIS
Petunia
CHRISTINA GILES
Zinnia
KATHERINE GILES
Victoria
STEPHANIE RALPH

Production Manager
DAVID NOBLE
1st Assistant Director
IAN MORLEY
Location Manager
MENZIES KENNEDY
Stage Manager
ANTON DARBY
Production Assistant
LIZ WADDELL
Unit Assistant
STUART BARLOW
Production Secretary
KAREN BARKER
Stills Photographer
ROB EBDON
Production Buyer
BOB BAYNE
Chargehand Props
DAVE PROCTOR
Chargehand Electrician
MAL IRWIN
Camera Operator
DAVE CAREY
Sound Recordist
LEE CORBETT
Dubbing Mixer
STEVE HAYNES
Dubbing Editor
ROY LAFBERY
Titles
PAUL PEPPIATE
Casting
MALCOLM DRURY
Costume Designer
BRIAN CASTLE
Make Up Designer
PAM FOX
Title Music
PIP BURLEY
Music
BARRIE GUARD
Editor
IAN MALLETT
Designer
ALAN DAVIS
Director of Photography
PETER JACKSON BSC
Produced in association with
EXCELSIOR GROUP PRODUCTIONS
Executive Producers
VERNON LAWRENCE
RICHARD BATES

THE DARLING BUDS OF MAY EPISODE THREE

Adapted by Bob Larbey
Producer Robert Banks Stewart
Director Robert Tronson

Pop Larkin
DAVID JASON
Ma Larkin
PAM FERRIS
Charley
PHILIP FRANKS
Mariette
CATHERINE ZETA JONES
Brigadier
MORAY WATSON
Edith Pilchester
RACHEL BELL
Sir George Bluff-Gore
MICHAEL CULVER
Lady Bluff-Gore
RICHENDA CAREY

Mr Jerebohm
JOHN GRILLO
Mrs Jerebohm
SUSIE BLAKE
Angela Snow
KIKA MIRYLEES
Uncle Perce
ARTHUR WHITE
Corinne Perigo
CELIA IMRIE
Mr Shell
PETER GALE
Mrs Hall
SHIRLEY CAIN
Countess Czernikov
JANE DOWNS
Aunt Bridget
JANE WENHAM
Building Society Manager
MICHAEL SHEARD
Bertie Fanshawe
IAN PRICE
Reverend Spink
JOHN CARLIN
Jim
TERENCE ORR
Hotel Commissionaire
HARRY BEETY
Montgomery
IAN TUCKER
Primrose
JULIE DAVIS
Petunia
CHRISTINA GILES
Zinnia
KATHERINE GILES
Victoria
STEPHANIE RALPH

Production Manager
DAVID NOBLE
1st Assistant Director
IAN MORLEY
Location Manager
MENZIES KENNEDY
Stage Manager
ANTON DARBY
Production Assistant
PATRICIA BELL
Unit Assistant
STEPHEN CONS
Production Secretary
KAREN BARKER
Production Buyer
BOB BAYNE
Chargehand Props
DAVE PROCTOR
Chargehand Electrician
MAL IRWIN
Camera Operator
DAVE CAREY
Sound Recordist
LEE CORBETT
Dubbing Mixer
STEVE HAYNES
Dubbing Editor
RICHARD SKELTON
Graphics
PAUL PEPPIATE
Casting
MALCOLM DRURY
Costume Designer
BRIAN CASTLE
Make Up Designer
PAM FOX
Title Music
PIP BURLEY
Music
BARRIE GUARD
Editor
PETER TAYLOR
Designer
ALAN DAVIS
Director of Photography
PETER JACKSON BSC
Produced in association with
EXCELSIOR GROUP
PRODUCTIONS
Executive Producers
VERNON LAWRENCE
RICHARD BATES

THE DARLING BUDS
OF MAY
EPISODE FOUR

Adapted by Bob Larbey
Producer Robert Banks
Stewart
Director Robert Tronson

Pop Larkin
DAVID JASON
Ma Larkin
PAM FERRIS
Charley
PHILIP FRANKS
Mariette
CATHERINE ZETA JONES
The Brigadier
MORAY WATSON
Edith Pilchester
RACHEL BELL
Sir George Bluff-Gore
MICHAEL CULVER
Lady Bluff-Gore
RICHENDA CAREY
Mr Jerebohm
JOHN GRILLO
Mrs Jerebohm
SUSIE BLAKE
Angela Snow
KIKA MIRYLEES
Uncle Perce
ARTHUR WHITE
Corinne Perigo
CELIA IMRIE
Captain Perigo
GAVIN GRAINGER
Bertie Fanshawe
IAN PRICE
Countess Czernikov
JANE DOWNS
Reverend Spink
JOHN CARLIN
Ingrid
HARRIET HARRISON
Mr Barlow
RON MEADOWS
Clerk of the Court
BRIAN BAINES
Sergeant Wilson
MARTYN READ
Court Usher
ANTHONY WINGATE
Hotel Commissionaire
HARRY BEETY
Montgomery
IAN TUCKER
Primrose
JULIE DAVIS
Petunia
CHRISTINA GILES
Zinnia
KATHERINE GILES
Victoria
STEPHANIE RALPH

Production Manager
DAVID NOBLE
1st Assistant Director
IAN MORLEY
Location Manager
MENZIES KENNEDY
Stage Manager
ANTON DARBY
Production Assistant
PATRICIA BELL
Unit Assistant
STEPHEN CONS
Production Secretary
KAREN BARKER
Production Buyer
BOB BAYNE
Chargehand Props
DAVE PROCTOR
Chargehand Electrician
MAL IRWIN
Camera Operator
DAVE CAREY
Sound Recordist
LEE CORBETT
Dubbing Mixer
STEVE HAYNES
Dubbing Editor
RICHARD SKELTON
Graphics
PAUL PEPPIATE
Casting
MALCOLM DRURY
Costume Designer
BRIAN CASTLE
Make Up Designer
PAM FOX
Title Theme
PIP BURLEY
Music
BARRIE GUARD
Editor
PETER TAYLOR
Designer
ALAN DAVIS
Director of Photography
PETER JACKSON BSC
Produced in association with
EXCELSIOR GROUP
PRODUCTIONS
Executive Producers
VERNON LAWRENCE
RICHARD BATES

THE DARLING BUDS
OF MAY
EPISODE FIVE

Adapted by Robert Banks
Stewart
Producer Richard Bates
Director David Giles

Pop Larkin
DAVID JASON
Ma Larkin
PAM FERRIS
Charley
PHILIP FRANKS
Mariette
CATHERINE ZETA JONES
Mlle. Dupont
ANNA MASSEY
Monsieur Mollet
CHARLES KAY
Angela Snow
KIKA MIRYLEES
Iris Snow
JUDY CLIFTON
Gerard Brisson
GEOFFREY GREENHILL
Monsieur Gammelin
PETER SYMONDS
Madame Gammelin
MARILYN TAYLERSON
Auctioneer
PHILIP ROWLANDS
Attendant
PHILIP WILDE
Cordelia
MITZI MCKENZIE
Maurice
DOC O' BRIEN
Sebastian
LAURENT HENNEQUIN
Inspecteur
BERT GAUNT
Montgomery
IAN TUCKER
Primrose
JULIE DAVIS
Marc-Antoine
CHRISTOPHER
HARRINGTON
Petunia
CHRISTINA GILES
Zinnia
KATHERINE GILES
Victoria
STEPHANIE RALPH
Oscar
ROSS MARRIOTT

Production Manager
DAVID NOBLE

1st Assistant Director
IAN MORLEY
Location Managers
MENZIES KENNEDY
PASCAL LEMAITRE
Stage Manager
ANTON DARBY

Production Assistant
SARAH COCKCROFT
Unit Assistant
STEPHEN CONS
Production Secretary
KAREN BARKER
Production Buyer
BOB BAYNE
Chargehand Props
DAVE PROCTOR
Chargehand Electrician
MAL IRWIN
Camera Operator
DAVE CAREY
Sound Recordist
LEE CORBETT
Dubbing Mixer
STEVE HAYNES
Dubbing Editor
ALAN WILLIS
Graphics
PAUL PEPPIATE
Casting
MALCOLM DRURY
SUE JACKSON
GERARD MOULEVREIR
Costume Designer
BRIAN CASTLE
Make Up Designer
PAM FOX
Title Theme
PIP BURLEY
Music
BARRIE GUARD
Editor
DAVID ASPINALL
Designer
ALAN DAVIS
Director of Photography
PETER JACKSON BSC
Produced in association with
EXCELSIOR GROUP
PRODUCTIONS
Executive Producers
VERNON LAWRENCE
PHILIP BURLEY
© YTV 1991

THE DARLING BUDS OF MAY
EPISODE SIX

Adapted by Robert Banks Stewart
Producer Richard Bates
Director David Giles

Pop Larkin
DAVID JASON
Ma Larkin
PAM FERRIS
Charley
PHILIP FRANKS
Mariette
CATHERINE ZETA JONES
Mlle. Dupont
ANNA MASSEY

Monsieur Mollet
CHARLES KAY
Angela Snow
KIKA MIRYLEES
Iris Snow
JUDY CLIFTON
Gerard Brisson
GEOFFREY GREENHILL
Monsieur Gammelin
PETER SYMONDS
Madame Gammelin
MARILYN TAYLERSON
Cordelia
MITZI MCKENZIE
Gabby
JOHN MORENO
Maxine
HELEN COOPER
Alphonse
GEORGES TRILLAT
Pierre
ALAIN FLICK
Sebastian
LAURENT HENNEQUIN
Montgomery
IAN TUCKER
Primrose
JULIE DAVIS
Marc-Antoine
CHRISTOPHER HARRINGTON
Petunia
CHRISTINA GILES
Zinnia
KATHERINE GILES
Victoria
STEPHANIE RALPH
Oscar
ROSS MARRIOTT

Production Manager
DAVID NOBLE
1st Assistant Director
IAN MORLEY
Location Managers
MENZIES KENNEDY
PASCAL LEMAITRE
Stage Manager
ANTON DARBY
Production Assistant
SARAH COCKCROFT
Unit Assistant
STEPHEN CONS
Production Accountant
ABU MOMONIAT
Production Secretary
KAREN BARKER
Production Buyer
BOB BAYNE
Assistant Designer
LOU BEAUMONT
Chargehand Props
DAVE PROCTOR
Chargehand Electrician
MAL IRWIN
Camera Operator
DAVE CAREY
Focus Puller
JOHN PINKNEY
Grip
KEVIN BINNS
Clapper Loader
ANN MAGUIRE
Sound Recordist
LEE CORBETT
Boom Operator
JIM RANYARD
Assistant Film Editor
JOHN WADDINGTON
Telecine Colouriser
IAN MORTIMER
Dubbing Mixer
STEVE HAYNES
Dubbing Editor
ROY LAFBERY
Casting
MALCOLM DRURY
SUE JACKSON
GERARD MOULEVREIR
Costume Designer
BRIAN CASTLE
Costume Supervisor
JANICE MARSDEN
Make Up Designer
PAM FOX
Graphics
PAUL PEPPIATE
Title Theme
PIP BURLEY
Music
BARRIE GUARD
Editor
DAVID ASPINALL
Designer
ALAN DAVIS
Director of Photography
PETER JACKSON BSC
Produced in association with
EXCELSIOR GROUP
PRODUCTIONS
Executive Producers
VERNON LAWRENCE
PHILIP BURLEY
© YTV 1991

WITH THE EXCEPTION OF THE PICTURES LISTED BELOW ALL THE PRODUDCTION STILLS IN THE BOOK ARE THE COPYRIGHT OF YORKSHIRE TELEVISION

p.9 Norman Brand
p.10 Richard Bates
p.11 Richard Bates
p.12 Topham Picture Source
p.13 Richard Bates
p.14 Richard Bates
p.15 Topham Picture Source
p.16 Richard Bates
p.17 Richard Bates
p.19 Norman Brand
p.21 Norman Brand
p.23 Norman Brand
p.37 Norman Brand
p.39 Norman Brand
p.42 Norman Brand
p.52 Norman Brand
p.55 E.T. Archive
p.57 Norman Brand
p.73 Norman Brand
p.75 Norman Brand
p.93 Norman Brand
p.111 Norman Brand
p.121 E.T. Archive
p.125 Norman Brand